Light Over Fatima

By

Charles C. O'Connell

Light Over Fatima

By

Charles C. O'Connell

THE NEWMAN PRESS
WESTMINSTER, MARYLAND
1948

901

FIRST PUBLISHED IN U.S.A. 1948.

TO

MY

MOTHER.

ACKNOWLEDGMENT

I acknowledge my indebtedness to Kevin J. Kenny, Esq., Portuguese Hon. Vice-Consul; Dr. Antero Carreiro de Freitas, Portuguese Charge d'Affaires, and Very Rev. Dr. Manuel Marques dos Santos, Vic. General, Cova da Iria, Fatima, Editor of " Voz da Fatima " (Spanish-English Edition), who, in spite of their many duties, found time to supply me with very valuable information.

I am happy to record here my deep debt of gratitude to Capt. J. M. Feehan, Director of The Mercier Press, Cork. Were it not for his unfailing interest, constant encouragement and advice, this book might never have found its way into print.

I also wish to thank Miss Una Morrissy for her excellent work on the final manuscript.

CHARLES C. O'CONNELL.

CHAPTER ONE.

LUCIA dos Santos anxiously scanned the sky and blinked under the lightly falling rain. The sun was still shining, but a huge cloud, spreading fanwise from the crest of Cabeço, was sending the harbingers of a downpour riding on the breeze. On the skyline the old windmill had ceased its laboured turning to raise its canvas arms as if in mute appeal to the darkening sky. The flock of sheep, cropping almost desperately at the scanty growth, had scattered all over the hillside. Some, indeed, had wandered as far as the screen of olive trees which filled a small notch in the extreme western end of the pasture. Others had breasted the steep incline and were already within the creeping shadow of the cloud overhead.

The girl adjusted her woollen headkerchief over her raven hair and gazed about. Although she was not yet nine years old she was wise in weather lore and knew from experience the relentless quality of the Spring rain in these uplands. Some distance away her cousin, Jacinta Marto, was also looking at the threatening cloud. Lucia called to her: " It's going to rain, Jacinta. Where's Francisco? "

Jacinta, fully a head shorter than her cousin and nearly three years younger, glanced about indifferently and shrugged. " I don't know. We'd better see to the sheep without him."

1

With stealthy precision the cloud finally obliterated the sun and the rain began to thicken. Working from adjacent sides the children startled the sheep into an uncertain scamper towards the trees. Elf-like, their full peasant skirts flying, they darted about their charges ever compressing them into a compact mass of shaggy plaintiveness.

" I wonder where Francisco can be? " Lucia voiced her anxiety some time later when Jacinta had once more come within hailing distance. " I hope nothing has happened to him? " Visibility had become so restricted that she could no longer see the distant steeple of Fatima, and the great mill on the crest of Cabeço was disappearing, like a frustrated giant, in the mist.

" Don't worry about him," said Jacinta in a disgusted tone. " He'll turn up when the work is done." She was all too familiar with the exasperating irresponsibility of her brother.

Even as she finished speaking the truant appeared, running furiously, his black stocking cap rising and falling on his shoulders as he bounded along. He was panting when he reached the girls though he tried to conceal it by a dogged breath control. Fully as tall as Lucia, his somewhat pretentious air was emphasised by his long staff and the gaily tasselled horn slung over his shoulder.

Jacinta eyed him severely. " Where have you been? Don't you know it's going to pour? "

Francisco wiped his damp face with the trailing end of his cap and returned his sister's stare with studied indifference. Then, prodding his staff into the pelt of a lagging sheep, " This is only a Spring shower," he said, in tones which plainly showed his contempt for all feminine alarmists.

" Even so," interposed Lucia, " we'll be soaked before we reach the cave."

Her prediction proved incorrect but scarcely had they manoeuvred the small flock into the depression when the rain came down in torrents, beating a merciless tattoo on the olive leaves. The children ran for shelter.

The cave of Cabeço was almost hidden among the trees. It was nothing more than a deep hole gouged in the granite wall of the notch but it constituted the sole advantage of this pasture over those of Cova da Iria and Valinhos, both of which were nearer to Fatima but lacking in any protection against the Spring squalls. The smell of dank earth permeated the interior of the hole and from somewhere in the darkness of the roof, water was constantly seeping. It gleamed on the rocky walls and produced a slimy green growth that was cold and unpleasant to touch. Some crisp leaves and long withes covered the centre of the floor but near the walls the leaves had become sodden and emitted the sharp, sweet odour of decay.

Francisco pulled off his stocking cap and shook it vigorously. His sister flinched from the flying moisture. " Aren't we wet enough? "

Francisco only laughed. " A little water won't hurt you."

Lucia was ruefully drying her forelocks in her

headkerchief. "We wouldn't be wet at all if you had been there to help us," she told her cousin bluntly. She was not angry. Her irritability was caused more by the sight of the boy's damp clothes than by his habitual indolence. The long checked trousers which clung closely to his legs and wrinkled over his stout boots looked wet and uncomfortable. Fortunately his frieze jacket was of stouter material, and had not even absorbed the rain which still gleamed on the dark material in crystalline beads. Francisco himself, idly tracing his staff among the dead leaves, seemed quite unconcerned either about his condition or his cousin's reproof.

Jacinta, usually the most talkative, had apparently forgotten about the rain, although her clothes were scarcely as adequate as her brother's. In spite of her delicate features and natural pallor, which differed sharply from the plain swarthiness of her cousin, she seemed a strong child.

Her smooth, dark hair, parted in the centre, peasant-fashion, and the serious expression of her brown eyes, gave her an appearance of startling maturity. The tip of a little pink tongue protruded now as she struggled to untie the neck of a cloth bundle she had drawn from the depths of her voluminous skirt. She succeeded at last in unfastening the cloth, and gravely apportioned the bread it contained to her two companions.

The lunch was small but it was allotted its full measure of respectful concentration. Save for the sound of the falling rain the silence was unbroken until every crumb had been eaten. It was only then that the restive Francisco went out to investigate the weather. The rain had ceased and the sun was making valiant efforts to pierce a procession of fleecy clouds. Some of the sheep had already wandered on to the pasture.

"The rain has stopped," the boy announced over his shoulder, "and the sheep are straying. We'd better get out."

Lucia smoothed her skirt. "Not until we say the Rosary," she said firmly.

Francisco looked at her in dismay. "Must we?"

Jacinta, already on her knees, looked at him from her deep eyes. "If you don't want to say it, Francisco, you may go."

"But it's so long." Francisco felt that he was appealing to their common sense. "Besides, I told you the sheep are straying."

The two girls exchanged a troubled glance. Lucia thought for a moment. Ever since she could remember the Rosary had been an integral part of her daily life, yet the long procession of Aves, interspaced by the more intricate Lord's Prayer, was, even to her, an exacting recitation. At home in Aljustrel, when her father's deep voice intoned the prayer, she often felt her mind receding until the voice rumbled as from a great distance, and the beads no longer slipped in correct sequence through her fingers. Secretly she almost welcomed Francisco's resistance.

"We'll say 'Hail Mary, Holy Mary' on each bead," she compromised at length, glancing almost apologetically at Jacinta. " After all, the sheep *are* straying."

Jacinta lifted her shoulders in indifferent acquiescence. Francisco, enjoying his moment of triumph, knelt on one knee at the mouth of the cave and waited for his cousin to begin. He blessed himself hurriedly and murmured the short responses in an undertone, twisting his head around repeatedly to view the sheep. At the Lord's Prayer he mumbled inarticulately, and hurried through the last decade so much that the tempo of the already abbreviated Rosary increased, and Lucia finished in breathless confusion. Francisco was the first from the cave.

The sun was shining brightly now and the dark cloud seemed but a low shadow over Fatima. The rain-washed air smelled fresh and clean and the green pasture had a brighter hue. Lucia lifted her face to the warming rays of the sun and shook her damp hair free. Even as she did so the long ringlets were blown about her cheeks by a sudden, strong wind. It pushed at her back, dragged at the heavy folds of her skirt, and sent her headkerchief scurrying over the backs of the startled sheep. She saw Francisco grab frantically at his wildly flapping stocking cap and Jacinta stumble forward on her knees. The noise of rushing air grew to a mighty crescendo in her ears, then suddenly died, leaving her in an utter stillness.

Instinctively she turned about, some strange emotion, not unlike fear, struggling deep within her. She seemed unable to breathe freely and her gasps were short and laboured.

" What was that, Lucia? " She was only vaguely aware of Francisco's frightened whisper. A tingling expectancy had rivetted her eyes to the tops of the olive trees. A cloud was floating from the foliage. Yet it was unlike any cloud she had ever seen. It shimmered and dazzled in the sun, and was approaching with a smoothness like vapour before a gentle breeze.

Before her eyes the gossamer nebula slowly attained the outline of a youth. Never in her life had she seen anybody like him. As he drifted towards the ground he seemed aflame in a dazzling aura of light. The delicate, almost effeminate, features were like chiselled marble. A snow-white robe, girdled at the waist, reached from his shoulders to his naked feet.

Lucia stood in terror. Her heart seemed to have become the battleground of many opposing forces. A strange joy struggled with a deadly fear that urged her with imperative insistence to run away, yet her faculties seemed no longer under her control. Her spirit, completely detached from physical encumbrances, stared through her eyes.

" Don't be afraid." The finely-moulded lips had scarcely moved. " I will not harm you."

His musical tones transformed the Portuguese dialect and acted as a soothing balm on Lucia's throbbing nerves.

" I am the Angel of Peace."

An angel! Then he was from heaven, and heaven was the promised land to which God would one day bring all His faithful children. So Lucia's mother had told her on many occasions. Yet the child's fear remained.

The angel seemed to understand her mental confusion. A faint, reassuring smile hovered about his lips as he raised his hand in an inviting gesture.

" Please pray with me."

Mechanically, without taking her gaze from the shining countenance, Lucia reached for her beads. The angel's smile grew more friendly when he saw her gesture, but, as if in answer to her tacit question, he shook his head slightly. With a graceful movement, he joined his hands and knelt, bowing slowly until his forehead touched the damp grass.

" My God," his voice came with unspeakable reverence, " I believe, I adore, I hope, I love You. I ask pardon for those who do not believe, nor hope, nor love You."

He repeated the prayer three times, then, rising with the same effortless grace, he faced the children.

" Pray in this manner. The Hearts of Jesus and Mary will allow themselves to be touched by your supplication."

He raised his hand in benediction and even as he traced the sign of the cross he began to ascend, upwards and backwards, until features and form merged with the resplendent light around him and finally vanished over the trees.

With an effort that was almost physically painful, Lucia dragged her consciousness free from the depths of an inner daze. She felt suddenly exhausted, and yielding to a natural instinct, sank on to the grass.

Only when the Marto children followed her example did she become aware of their presence. Their scared, bloodless faces were oddly reassuring in so far as they destroyed the possibility of illusion on her part. Francisco was visibly shaken. Even his lips were drained of colour and the hand which still gripped the long staff shook in spite of his efforts to control it. Jacinta sat like one in a trance. The pallor of her face accentuated the dark lustre of her eyes which were still fixed on the spot where the angel disappeared. Lucia had to tug at her skirt to attract her attention, and was rewarded only with a vacant stare.

" We must not tell anybody of this," said Lucia urgently. " No one would believe us." She could not be sure of the effect of her words, but she knew that if that inner voice, which even now was whispering in her heart, were reproduced in the breasts of her cousins, they would remain silent to the grave.

CHAPTER TWO.

THE hamlet of Aljustrel straggled for a dusty kilometre along the mountain road from Ourem to Leiria. Officially the place was forgotten, being completely eclipsed by the more compact neighbouring village of Fatima, which boasted a church and presbytery, a school-house, an inferior hotel and a slightly lesser degree of isolation. On the Prefect's administrative map at Santarem, Aljustrel and Fatima were represented by a single dot superscribed with the name of the latter. The identification was accepted by the peasant population of the district, with the solitary exception, perhaps, of Antonio dos Santos, who was apt to be argumentative on this point of high principle. He would point out the distinction between the purely dependent population of Fatima and the farming community of Aljustrel. He would contrast, to the detriment of the villagers, the degrading occupation of goat herding with the ageless dignity of farming. Sometimes, when native wine warmed his deliberations, his small holding would expand itself to a vast acreage, straddling the snowcapped Serra d'Estrella, and his flock of thirty sheep would multiply themselves to as many thousands. This process of imaginative inflation was applied quite successfully to his colourful presentation of a farmer's heart-breaking labour to feed the idle mouths of Fatima. He would draw attention

10

to the premature wrinkles on his strong, tanned face, and display the callouses of his gnarled hands, rough with honest toil. But were any of his listeners to see him on this summer day, the entertainment value of his habitual discourse would be appreciably enhanced.

He sat under the awning of the outshed and puffed contentedly at his pipe. Never had he remembered such a day! Not a breath of wind relieved the heavy air. At the end of the acreage the tall pine trees, that stood sentinel over the well, seemed to be wilting before his very eyes. To the north, the outline of the serrated peaks had merged with the universal white glare, except where a facet of snow, bending the sun's rays, shone like a mirror in the sky. Certainly, it was never intended that men should work in such heat, and, in spite of his dogmatic assertions, Antonio dos Santos scorned drudgery.

It was characteristic of him that he preserved a fine sense of balance where labour was concerned. He worked hard, but never too hard, and on days like this he did not work at all. An even distribution among his family of the agrarian tasks of his holding ensured that certain days could be spent in idleness without seriously jeopardising his varied though meagre crops. So he rested with an easy conscience and idly watched the heat waves distort the landscape. And presently he slept.

He was awakened by the bleating of many sheep. For a moment his heavy eyes refused to focus in the bright light and while he knuckled them vigorously his wife's voice sounded, loud and hard.

" I was hoping you'd come back."

Then another voice which he recognised as Lucia's:
" The Cova was like a frying-pan, Mamma, and the
sheep need water."

Antonio grimaced at the last words and drew
himself up stiffly. Some yards away Lucia and the
Marto children were standing among the sheep. His
wife, who had just come from the house, was drying her
hands in her apron. He strode across towards them.

Lucia turned as he approached. " It was scorching
at the Cova, Papa. We had to come home before we
fried."

Her father viewed the sheep without enthusiasm.
Most of them had squatted on the ground, too
exhausted to do more than breathe. The pasture at
Cova da Iria and Cabeço would be scorched if this
weather lasted. Maybe he would take four or six of
the animals to the fair at Ourem at the end of the
month. His annoyance at the disturbance of his sleep
was softened by the exhausted appearance of the
children. Lucia was unusually flushed, and Francisco
kept rubbing his sleeve across his forehead. Jacinta, her
natural pallor unaltered, was the only one of the trio
who looked cool.

" All right, children," Antonio hitched his belt.
" Run and play now. I'll see to the sheep."

He watched them scamper towards the well, where
the trees provided the only outdoor shade on the farm
to-day, smiling at their eagerness. Then, noticing the
expression on his wife's face, he said: " Don't worry
about them, Mamma. A little heat won't harm them."

His wife looked at him a moment without speaking. She was not a big woman, but her rigid carriage gave her the appearance of being taller than she actually was. At times there was a direct imperiousness about her gaze which he found disconcerting. In the years of their life together she had given him much to admire: her unrelenting industry; her pride in respectability with its horror of ridicule; her impeccable piety that emphasised the fear of God. Antonio went a little in awe of her, but, although he could not understand her moods, he could readily recognise them. When she was anxious or worried, two lines formed above the bridge of her nose and drew her eyebrows together—just as they were now, for his assurance of a moment before had left her features unrelieved.

" Have you noticed that Lucia has changed? " she asked suddenly.

The man stared after the children again. " Changed? In what way? "

" Oh, nothing physical. She is "—Senhora Santos seemed to have difficulty in finding the right words— " well, she's quieter, for one thing."

Antonio clapped his hands sharply and startled the sheep to their feet. " The child is growing, Mamma. Changes are bound to come. It is natural. You don't think she will remain a child always? "

His wife made a gesture of annoyance.

" It's not just her quietness," she told him. " It's some queer mood that has gripped her since early Spring. Once "—her voice became hesitant—" I saw her kneel on the ground—and bow like a heathen! "

" Nothing but some childish game," the man answered carelessly. " She looks well enough." He could see that his wife was not convinced and he shrugged his broad shoulders. The mentality of all women, but particularly that of his own wife, was something he would never understand. They created substance from shadows. His daughter appeared perfectly normal to him, nor had he noticed any change in her beyond the normal physical development which, somehow, never failed to surprise him. He had rarely seen Lucia or her cousins in any but a happy mood.

" I don't think it was a game," the woman persisted, more to herself than to her husband. " She had the oddest expression on her face."

Antonio was wise enough to let her have the last word.

Meanwhile Francisco and Jacinta Marto were leaning on the stone parapet of the well and gazing down at the dark surface of the water. Their young faces, mirrored below, stared happily up at them. Occasionally, from high in the side of the well, a drop of water would fall musically into the pool, destroying all semblance of normality in the reflected faces. Slowly the ringlets of water would cease their radiation and the picture once again appear, well defined, only to be instantly shattered by the relentless seepage.

Lucia had tired of the sport. She leaned listlessly against the stones and idly fingered the frayed edge of her headkerchief. Even here among the trees the heat induced a state of semi-torpor. She felt completely

drained of energy, yet some uneasy presentiment kept
her eyes moving in restless watchfulness. The cheerful
chatter of her companions irked her strangely and
created an unaccountable sense of isolation. This
strange irritability grew and changed until it attained,
in a succession of varying sensations, the riotous
emotions experienced for the first time, months ago, on
the hill of Cabeço.

Her mood seemed to transmit itself to the Marto
children. Their sport suddenly lost its appeal, but not
until the dark interior of the well was illuminated, as
by a torch held overhead, did they look up.

The Angel of Peace stood before them and the
grove was flooded with light! The look of mild
reproach on the angel's face was unmistakable.

" What are you doing? "

Three minds strove to form an answer, but the
musical voice deterred them.

" Pray—pray a great deal. The Hearts of Jesus
and Mary have merciful designs on you." His voice
dropped to a note of entreaty. " Will you not offer
prayers and sacrifices continually to God in reparation
for the numerous sins which offend Him—and in
supplication for the conversion of sinners? "

To Lucia it seemed that she sensed rather than
heard the words. Her perceptions had become so keen
that words were no longer necessary. The thoughts of
the angel simply flowed to her.

Her own spoken question was barely whispered.
" How are we to make sacrifices? "

The angel seemed pleased with her question. A

tender smile relieved the solemnity of his expression.

"Make everything you do a sacrifice. Offer it as an act of reparation for the sins of the world. Try in this way to bring peace to your country. . . . I am its Angel Guardian." The musical voice softened once more to pleading. "Above all, children, accept and bear with submission the sufferings which it will please God to send you."

For a moment after he had finished speaking he stood in an attitude of deep prayer. Then his lucent outline began to fade. Yet before he merged completely with the air above them, he raised his hand in a parting benediction that appeared to hang for a moment in the air, like a cross of light.

From beyond the shade the loud voice of Senhor Santos was raised in passionate appeal to the exhausted sheep.

CHAPTER THREE.

AS the hot summer months passed the change in Lucia became more apparent to Senhora Santos. Physically the child was perfectly healthy, in fact, she showed visible improvement, thereby belying any suggestion of some unknown malady. Yet her mother was convinced that, since the previous Spring, her daughter had not been the same. She was quieter, more subdued, given to long day dreams, during which her eyes seemed not to see those around her and the little plain face became that of a stranger's. Tasks and errands that some months before had caused sulky dissension were now performed with a certain joyful eagerness. Even her manner of speech had become more refined, more gentle.

The very fact that she could not explain this change, made Senhora Santos harsh towards Lucia, and, to a lesser degree, towards her father. But she had more patience with him than with the girl. Not that Lucia had become a delinquent—on the contrary, her perfect conduct would have been any mother's pride if it were not so unnatural. So the woman reasoned. Only in the wakeful hours of the night, when the gentle breathing of Lucia reached across the silent room, did remorse touch the heart of the Senhora. Then she would realise that her bitter treatment of her daughter was simply a vain effort to make the child revert to the once familiar ways which were not beyond the understanding of a mother. These reveries led to resolutions of amendment that dispersed, however, with the light of day.

Gradually, as the months went by, the gulf between mother and daughter widened. It seemed to the disconsolate woman that Lucia no longer belonged to her, and never was the realisation of this more poignant than on this afternoon as she watched her daughter and the Marto children driving the sheep along the road to Cabeço.

Ten year old Lucia, talking gaily to her companions, was completely unaware of the mental turmoil she was causing her mother. It was true that sometimes her parent's unaccountable anger puzzled and distressed her, but the hurt was completely eclipsed since it provided an opportunity to " accept and bear with submission " anything that it pleased God to send.

To-day she had not a single dismal thought. Never in her short life had she remembered being so happy, nor since her private Holy Communion at Fatima had such a feeling of happy anticipation filled her breast. There was a peculiar lightness in the air, and a special invigorating quality in the wind which blew gently from the snowcapped peaks. Her mood was infectious, for occasionally Jacinta's gay chatter changed to a lively tune, and her dancing feet caused a minor stampede among the sheep.

Francisco seemed to be the only member of the trio to whom the magic of the day was not apparent. Of late he had grown morose, and had developed a habit of glancing uneasily about as if he expected to find someone at his elbow. He spoke but rarely, and even then with a crispness that discouraged further conversation. Yet, when at length the sheep ambled on to the pasture at Cabeço, even he had relented a little. He pulled off his stocking cap and shook his unruly hair free in the wind, then looked at his sister with all his old arrogant confidence.

" I'll race you to the tree, Jacinta? "

His sister eyed him a moment. " If you give me a start? "

The boy nodded confidently and Jacinta shot away like a young hare. Her brother allowed her a generous lead, then, discarding his long staff, darted after her.

The finish of the race was close, but with unusual magnanimity. Francisco conceded the victory to his sister. It was a manifestation of his new mood which lasted all the afternoon and only evaporated when Lucia, glancing at the lowering sun, suggested they go to the cave.

The boy came to his feet. To go to the cave meant to pray, for the spot had now become their special shrine where they could kneel as the Angel had taught them without fear of being observed by passing shepherds. For Francisco the daily routine was becoming a burdensome duty. Prayer was all right for girls, but now that the memory of the Angel had grown dim he was convinced that a man should be occupied with more practical things. Nevertheless his only sign of disapproval was a sudden gravity that set his features in an almost grim cast.

Inside the cave Lucia began their abbreviated form of the Rosary. No attempt had been made to reintroduce the longer form, since now they had added the angel's prayer to their liturgy. But they had learned to say the short ejaculations with becoming reverence and without their previous haste.

The Rosary ended, Lucia, without shifting her position, bowed until her forehead touched the ground. Her cousins followed her example and three muffled, reverent voices recited the prayer of the angel, ' My God, I believe, I adore, I hope, I love You." Even as her forehead touched the cold earth Lucia became aware of a sudden brightening of the interior of the cave. The light, which came from nowhere, grew in intensity until even the rocky walls were lost in its blazing grandeur. Under its mysterious glow Jacinta's rough apparel resembled a beautiful gown of unknown material. Her little hands were joined at her breast and her eyes had captured the lustre of the glory about her. Francisco kneeling beyond her was praying quietly.

Involuntarily Lucia's eyes were drawn to where the mouth of the cave had been. A rising sensation of wonder caused her breath to come rapidly; a figure was materialising before her. Slowly the outline of robe and features emerged from the air, attaining, at length, the familiar form of the Angel of Peace. Never had he seemed more beautiful. He was brighter than the light about them and in his hands he bore a chalice surmounted by a Host which seemed to be the source of all this glory.

Many times at Mass in Fatima, when the consecration bell had bowed a sea of heads, Lucia had dared raise her eyes. She had seen the Holy Bread, circular, white, familiar, and the chalice, gleaming in the light of the altar candles. But the chalice and Host before her now were different from any she had ever seen in the consecrated hands of Dom Agostinho. The vessel was of purest gold, and from the centre of the snow-white Leaven, great drops of crimson Blood welled and fell into the chalice beneath.

For a long moment the angel stood with eyes reverently downcast. Then slowly he withdrew his fingers from the stem and Lucia's heart bounded in horror, expecting the precious vessel to fall. But miraculously it hung in the air, emanating a glow that shone even in the dazzling brightness about them. Lucia felt a strange urge within her which became almost physically painful. She scarcely noticed the angel had knelt beside her, and only when he spoke did she tear her eyes from the Host.

" Repeat after me," his voice was softly modulated, " Most Holy Trinity, Father, Son and Holy Ghost, I adore You profoundly. I offer you the most precious Body and Blood, Soul and Divinity, of Jesus Christ present in all the tabernacles of the world in reparation for the insults, sacrileges and indifferences whereby He is offended. By the infinite merits of His Most Sacred Heart and of the Immaculate Heart of Mary I beg of You the conversion of sinners."

Haltingly, sentence by sentence, the children

repeated the prayer and remained kneeling when the angel arose and approached the chalice. With deep veneration he took the vessel in his hands and turned about, just as Dom Agostinho did at the chapel of Fatima when the people crowded to the altar rails. Lucia hardly breathed as the angel approached her. She seemed to be re-living the day when she knelt before the tabernacle to receive her First Holy Communion. She had been conscious then of other things beside the Sacred Host; the snow-white altar cloth; her pretty cotton gloves; the pride of her mother seated with the watching congregation; the majestic appearance of the Parish Priest whom she had never seen quite so close before. But now all her faculties were concentrated on the Bread held between the angel's thumb and finger, and a burning spiritual hunger seemed to consume her. She shut her eyes and tilted her chin. The voice of the angel seemed like distant music.

"Receive the Body and Blood of Jesus Christ horribly outraged by ungrateful men. Make reparation for their sins and console your God."

The angel moved to Jacinta. The soul of the child was in her shining eyes. She offered eager lips to the chalice.

Lucia bowed her head. The realisation that her two companions were sharing in this wonderful gift overflowed her cup of delight. The voice of the angel reached through her ecstasy: "Most Holy Trinity, Father, Son and Holy Ghost, I adore You profoundly."

*   *   *   *   *

The last vestige of light had faded from the high horizon. A cold wind already portending the winter snows sighed fitfully in the darkness, creaking some unfastened gate, and tugging with icy fingers at Senhora Santos' shawl.

The woman stood in the middle of the road. Behind her the bright oblong of the lighted window alone relieved the gloom. She had been standing thus since darkness had fallen, a prey to nameless fears. Every sound of the countryside by night brought an ominous conjecture to her overwrought mind. She never remembered the children being so long at the pastures. Twilight, even in this season, invariably found them at home in bed. But it was almost an hour now since the sun had disappeared behind the high serra, and to the lonely woman watching, each dragging moment seemed an anxious eternity.

As she fought the impulse to rush along towards Cabeço the door of the house opened and her husband appeared. He had laughed at her fears earlier, but now the collar of his coat was turned up and his voice held an unusual tenseness.

" I'll walk along a little way."

He passed beside her on to the road. " Don't worry, Mamma. If anything had happened, one of them would have come back."

" But what could be keeping them? "

Antonio did not answer. He dug his hands into his jacket pocket and walked into the darkness. The sound of his footsteps came echoing back long after he disappeared. The woman found herself listening to them. There was a certain comfort in their hurried beat. But gradually they faded and finally ceased and the night appeared to press closer around her.

The heavy tread was out of earshot but a few seconds when it sounded again, swifter now, and accompanied by the unmistakable bleating of sheep.

In the darkness of the road Senhora Santos' anxiety was changing to a rising anger. Mentally she framed all she would say. She would be patient, as a Christian mother ought to be, but this night would see the end of Lucia's tantrums. She would have to be punished, and severely if necessary, to bring her strange new spirit under subjection. There would be no more day dreaming, no more heathen games. The woman's impatience forced her to walk towards the approaching flock.

" Lucia? "

Her husband's big frame loomed out of the darkness. " They are all right, Mamma. They didn't know it was so late."

The woman found herself in the midst of the advancing sheep. She saw Francisco Marto walking with his sister, their faces like two pools of grey in the darkness.

" Lucia? " She was searching about for her daughter when, wholly unexpectedly, she found her in her arms. The child appeared to be crying and the little hands were icy.

Senhora Santos' anger instantly died. " What is it, child? "

" Oh, nothing's the matter, Mamma. It's only I'm

so happy." The child's voice was reassuring. The woman ran her fingers through her daughter's hair. Questions would come later and perhaps the answers would be just as enigmatic as in the past. But it no longer mattered. For the moment, at least, Lucia was where she had wanted her to be. She possessed her daughter once again.

CHAPTER FOUR.

THE day was May 13th, 1917. The winter snows had receded to the uppermost peaks of the serras leaving a trail of blossoms colouring the hedgerows and daily dotting the green pastures. Even in the gigantic bowl of Cova da Iria, hollowed by nature, with a fiery hand, in aeons past, the grass was brightly decked in summer array. The stunted holm oaks scattered haphazardly about the depression had a fresher hue and the scanty olive trees ruffled their new foliage and whispered in the mild wind. High above in the limpid blue, the sun, already nearing its zenith, crept steadily across the sky; the same sun that even now was drenching the pitted earth of Flanders and gleaming on the tense faces of watchful men who awaited Death; it brightened the shellholes where the dead, legs and arms asprawl, gazed, unseeing, at its glory; it filtered through the smoke of battle and found the scarlet poppy growing amid corruption just as it bathed the amphitheatre of Iria and flushed the cheeks of Francisco Marto labouring beneath the weight of an angular lump of quartz.

The boy's progress was slow but determined. A pink tongue was fiercely gripped between his teeth as he staggered with his load. Nor was he deterred by Lucia's complaints concerning the size of the stone. As self-appointed supervising mason he was the best judge

of the material for their projected shelter. He reached
the girls at length and with a sigh of relief dumped the
quartz on the ground.

" There! " He wiped his streaming forehead with
the end of his stocking cap.

Lucia and Jacinta stared at the stone without
enthusiasm. Already they had laid the first ring of
stones which marked the plan of their shelter, though
this, whether they knew it or not, was a violation of the
supervising mason's prerogative.

" It's flat stones we need," Jacinta told her brother,
resting for a moment on her heels.

Francisco could not recall just then the purported
use of the quartz, his sister and Lucia having destroyed
his plan by beginning erection in his absence, so he
surveyed their work with a fine show of masculine
contempt.

" There's no door," he announced after a moment,
with a superiority that drew Jacinta's brows together.

" It's going to be here," she told him, indicating a
space behind her where the ring of stones was broken.

Francisco moved to view the spot, and instantly
turned startled eyes to the sky. At the same time Lucia
started to her feet in alarm. Jacinta alone remained
unperturbed.

" What is it? "

" Lightning—I think," Lucia replied doubtfully.
It had seemed like lightning, yet not a cloud showed in
the sky. Francisco was puzzled, too, but he was
none-the-less certain of what he had seen. " It was

lightning all right," he assured them. " It went like that." He demonstrated with his hand.

Lucia looked again at the sky. The decision to go or stay rested with her. It was pleasant playing here in the sun, but several times before she had been caught in torrential showers on this exposed pasture. Besides, the Cova was all of two kilometres from Fatima. She hesitated a moment. The absence of cloud prompted her to remain. But then the high rim of the hollow shut off the northern sky. Maybe the storm clouds were hidden beyond the hill? A glance at the scattered sheep decided her.

" We'd better go home! "

Jacinta was disappointed, but not for a moment did she think of disobeying her cousin. In questions like this Lucia's decision was final. Still it was not without regret that she came to her feet. A second later a brilliant flash of light streaked across the sky.

All three had seen the lightning this time. Feverishly they rounded up the scattered flock keeping apprehensive eyes on the northern ridge, expecting any moment the cloudy blackness of the storm to invade the sky. Their frantic yells terrified the sheep into a mad stampede towards the centre of the depression.

As she hurried down the slope Lucia tried to analyse a strange sensation welling within her. Eight months had passed since she last experienced such a feeling, yet the passage of time had neither dimmed nor mitigated its memory . . . the cave of Cabeço flooded with light . . . the Angel offering the chalice to her cousins and her own reception of the bleeding

Host. Her emotions, indescribable then, were similar to those she was experiencing now. The portending storm was forgotten.

She stopped suddenly and looked at Jacinta. The child's deathly pallor and the expression of her shining dark eyes reflected her own bewilderment, while her rapt attention was given to something as yet unseen by her cousins. Half fearfully Lucia followed the younger girl's gaze. A little distance away grew a holm oak tree. The wind rustling through its foliage showed the pale underside of the evergreen leaves. Lucia felt her eyes drawn upwards to the top of the tree.

*   *   *   *   *

Francisco had reached the foot of the declivity before he realised that the girls were no longer with him. He turned about and stopped. It was nothing new to find Lucia and Jacinta on their knees. Prayer had become an essential part of their daily programme, but surely they realized that a storm was coming? He cupped his hands and called to them. The girls did not move. They were kneeling near the holm oak and staring at its topmost branches.

Francisco retraced his steps. As he neared his kneeling companions he was struck by the expression on their faces. He had never seen them look like this before. Something in the tenseness of their attitude compelled him to approach on tip-toe. Lucia was apparently talking to the tree.

" Shall I go to heaven? "

Francisco stared at the tree. Perhaps the angel had visited them again? But there was nothing to see. He strained his ears to catch the answer to Lucia's question. He heard nothing but he saw his cousin smile.

" Will Jacinta go? "

Again a breathless pause and then Jacinta clasped her hands to her breast.

" And Francisco? "

The boy knelt beside Lucia and tugged at the corner of her headkerchief. " What is it, Lucia? Is it the angel? I can't see anything."

His cousin glanced at him in wonder and immediately returned her gaze to the tree. " Why is it that Francisco cannot see you? "

With beating heart Francisco waited for the answer, eagerly scrutinising Lucia's face for an indication of the unseen person's reply. At length Lucia turned to him.

" The lady says that if you say the Rosary you will see her."

Francisco reached in his pocket for his Rosary. The beads were tangled but he began to pray even as he was trying to disentangle them, still keeping his gaze fixed on the tree. As he finished the first decade he became aware of a light near the top. Eagerly his eyes lifted and immediately recoiled before the dazzling figure that stood there.

On the top of the holm oak with her feet hidden among the nodding foliage was a beautiful lady. She seemed not many years older than Lucia. Her dress was as white as snow in sunshine and reached down in rippling folds to her feet. The golden cord which tied the delicate fabric at the neck ended in two tassels and swayed gently in the breeze. Her head was covered with a gossamer veil richly embroidered with gold, its delicate fabric enveloping the figure and trailing among the holm oak leaves. The lady's hands were reverently joined and a Rosary of bright pearls hung from them. At the end of the long beads a silver cross shone in the sunlight like a star.

Francisco gazed spellbound at the lady. He drank in her beauty and felt his heart swell with an insatiable longing. Yet despite her beauty he could discern an expression of strange sadness on her face, and his own spirit expanded in sympathy to its mute appeal. He heard Lucia speak again.

" Is little Maria das Neves, who died recently, in Heaven? "

Francisco waited to hear the answer, but although he saw the exquisitely moulded lips move, he heard nothing. Lucia and Jacinta alone heard the reply :

" Yes. She is in Heaven."

" And Amelia? "

The sad expression deepened on the lady's face.

" She will be in Purgatory until the world ends." Then, as though hastening to obliterate that painful picture : " Would you like to offer yourselves to God— to make sacrifices and accept willingly all the sufferings He may send you? "

" Oh, yes," Lucia breathed, confident that she was answering for all three. " We'd like that very much."

A tender smile relieved the lady's sad expression. " In this way you will make reparation for the sins whereby He is offended and intercede for the conversion of sinners."

Lucia felt the urge to say something; to convey some of the eagerness she felt to conform entirely with the lady's will. Words tumbled over each other in her mind and the very effort to express them held her speechless. But the lady seemed to understand. She smiled again and inclined her head in grateful recognition of the child's tacit offer.

Then she parted her hands as if to allow a beam of light, until then concealed, to bathe the children in its radiant glow.

They felt its embrace about them like a living presence. It was warmer than the sun, more intimate. It seemed to penetrate their bodies and flood them with an intoxicating warmth until it isolated them and the lady from the drabness of the Cova, and enclosed them in a world of shimmering glory. Through the golden sheen of the miraculous ray the lady looked even more beautiful and lovable than before. Her garments appeared to have dissolved in the light, leaving the shining countenance as the centre of all this splendour.

For a few short moments the light lasted, then as the lady joined her hands it gradually faded. Her lovely, veiled eyes swept the three upturned faces, then smilingly she inclined her head in an intimate gesture of farewell. Slowly she began to rise from the tree and ascend into the sky, drawing the wistful eyes of the children heavenwards. With aching hearts they watched the vision fade until it was finally lost in the blue infinity.

Francisco was the first to speak.

" Lucia, what did the lady say? "

Still on her knees, his cousin turned surprised eyes towards him. " Didn't you hear? "

Francisco shook his head dolefully. " But I saw her. Is she the Blessed Virgin? "

The same question was burning in Lucia's mind. " I don't know," she told him. " We must come here on this date for six months, then she will tell us who she is and what she wants."

Francisco's curiosity was not satisfied. " Did she say anything else? Please, Lucia, tell me."

Lucia came to her feet. " She told us that we must say the Rosary every day to bring peace to the world. And we must say it properly." She paused for a moment, considering the wisdom of telling the boy what concerned him. But she couldn't resist the entreaty of his eyes. " The lady is from Heaven, Francisco, and she said that Jacinta and I would go there "— Francisco's face greyed as she paused—" and that you would go there, too, but you must say many Rosaries."

Relief brought the colour flooding back to the boy's cheeks and his eyes were suddenly swimming. He held up his Rosary to the girls.

" Look," he said, " my beads were hopelessly tangled."

CHAPTER FIVE.

OLIMPIA Marto set her laden basket on the ground and wearily lifted the looped wire that fastened the gate. The old hinges protested loudly as she pushed the rickety frame. The cabin door opened and her daughter appeared on the narrow porch.

"I'll get the basket, Mamma."

Senhora Marto was too weary to show any surprise. She merely nodded her head and refastened the gate.

"You're home early, Jacinta. Is Francisco with you?"

"Yes, Mamma. We thought there was going to be a storm."

The woman drew a hand across her warm forehead. "A storm—Sancta Maria!—on such a day?"

"But we really did think so at first," persisted Jacinta. "That was before we saw the lady." She checked herself suddenly and lifted anxious eyes to her mother's face.

Senhora Marto nodded, and then as the word registered: "What lady?"

Jacinta hesitated. Lucia had told them to keep the lady a secret. She had pointed out that nobody would believe them. But then one's mother was different— she would believe her. For another moment the child swayed between loyalty to Lucia and a desire to share the glorious news with her parent. Then all restraint crumbled.

" Do you know whom we saw at the Cova to-day, Mamma? "

It was the child's expression more than the words that impressed her mother.

" Who was it, Jacinta? "

" The Blessed Virgin, Mamma! "

" Jacinta! " Of all the answers, this was the least expected. " You shouldn't say such things."

" But it's true, Mamma. I swear it. I saw her with my own eyes. She was beautiful—and she spoke to us."

Senhora Marto gazed down at the pale, eager face. Rarely had she seen her little girl look so beautiful, with the dark, ardent eyes pleading so eloquently for belief. She envied the youthful imagination that could fashion the image of the Mother of God with such realism from the arid earth of the Cova. Let her stay young then as long as she might. Disenchantment would come soon enough and with it the realisation that the Blessed Virgin would find a more congenial place to visit than among the straggling ferns of a mountain pasture. Still, it was a sweet thought. She smiled into the eyes of her daughter and cupped the little chin in her hand.

" Is my little one already a saint, then, that she should see the Blessed Virgin? "

The red blood rose in Jacinta's cheeks. " Oh, no— Francisco saw her, too, and so did Cousin Lucia."

" My! " The woman raised her eyebrows. " And what did she say to you three little saints? "

Jacinta took a deep breath, fortifying herself for a momentous announcement.

" She told us to say the Rosary every day."

Olimpia Marto took the basket from the child.
" That's very good, Jacinta." She passed towards the
house. On the porch she paused. " Don't go very far
now, chica. Your supper will be ready soon."

Jacinta felt very near to tears. Since she came
home from the Cova she had haunted the gate, waiting
for her mother to come from the village. She had
visualised the joy and wonder which her story of the
Blessed Virgin's visit would create. This was a bitter
anti-climax.

The lady was so real that Jacinta couldn't
understand how anybody could not credit her
appearance. Only then did the child realise that if her
mother denied the apparition she evidently thought that
the whole story was a wicked fabrication. The horror
of this thought drove Jacinta into the kitchen.

Senhora Marto was laying the table and she did not
look up when her daughter entered.

" Mamma," Jacinta's chin just cleared the edge of
the table. " You don't think I'm lying about the
Blessed Virgin? "

" Of course not, child—not deliberately, anyway.
Run now and find Francisco."

Jacinta's spirits rose. If her mother did not think
the lady was a lie, then she must believe. The situation
offered another opportunity of repeating the all
important message.

" She said that we must say the Rosary every day,
Mamma."

Her mother made an irritable gesture. " So you

told me, child. It's a very good thing to say your beads.
Now go and find Francisco."

Olimpia Marto watched her go. She wondered if
she faltered in parental duty by not punishing the child.
Now if it had been Francisco, with his reckless
irresponsibility, she would know what to do. But it
was obvious Jacinta believed what she said. To the
impressionable child a tree or stone had become a lady,
a wind in the tree, a voice—the Rosary was but
unconscious colouring. Ah, well! no harm would
come of such hallucinations provided they didn't
embrace the people of the nether regions. The woman
smiled at the thought.

She crossed to the back kitchen where to-day's
kindling lay piled against the wall. She collected an
armful and, as she straightened, glanced through the
open window.

Francisco and Jacinta were walking from around
the gable engrossed in earnest conversation. The boy
was growing more and more like his brother, Manuel.
Dear Manuel, that tall, strapping lad, so carelessly
debonair and yet so solicitous for her welfare. He had
gone cheerfully to a war of which he knew nothing.
She shrugged her angular shoulders. All things were
in the hands of God. Some day he would come back.

She reached a hand to close the window, then
suddenly paused. Outside, near the solitary pine which
threw its long shadow across the farmyard, her two
children were kneeling. The murmur of their young
voices reached the watching woman.

* * * * *

Manuel Pedro pushed his chair a little away from the table and looked uncertainly at his wife. During supper he had deliberated on all she had told him, but was no nearer a solution. Since it was a more or less religious matter, he felt that it lay rather within his wife's province. He looked across at Jacinta and Francisco, sitting together. They had eaten calmly and heartily, and were now awaiting their mother's command to withdraw.

Manuel Pedro cleared his throat and ruffled his moustache with a gnarled forefinger. " Suppose you tell us about your lady now, Jacinta."

The child's eyes brightened immediately. She threw a grateful glance at her mother and launched her story without the slightest hesitation. All the wonder and reverent awe she had felt in the Cova shone again in her face. Her eager voice rose and fell as her narration progressed, deepening with emotion, sinking to a whisper as she tried to describe the lady's ineffable beauty, almost breaking as she painted the intangible look of sorrow on the shining countenance. Francisco, looking now at his sister, now at the tense faces of his parents, remained silent. Jacinta had not finished before Manuel Pedro was convinced that something extraordinary had happened at Cova da Iria that day. No figment of the imagination could warrant such conviction in a seven year old child. Nobody but an actual eye-witness could have breathed such life into the spoken word. He knew her sufficiently well to realise she was not lying. Always impressionable, and with a great capacity for affection, she was nevertheless, a realist.

Only when she had finished did he question her. " Did the lady tell you she was the Blessed Virgin? "

" No," Jacinta answered immediately. " But she told us that she came from heaven."

Her father shifted his gaze to Francisco. " Did you hear the lady say she was the Blessed Virgin? "

The boy shook his head. " I only saw her, Papa. I didn't hear her speak."

" But the most important thing," Jacinta broke in suddenly, " was about the Rosary. The lady wants us to say it every day to bring peace to the world."

Olimpia Marto had long since left and Senhora table. Peace to the world! What could these children of hers know of war? She stared at the two tense faces. Their earnest innocence was unfeigned.

" If the Blessed Virgin has come down to tell my children to say the Rosary," she spoke almost to herself, " the entire family will say it from this very day."

* * * * *

Olimpia Marto's hands clutched at the edge of the Santos and her husband sat before the dead fire. The man puffed moodily at his pipe and yielded to his thoughts. The scene that had been enacted but an hour ago was totally beyond the gamut of his simple intelligence, yet in some vague way, he had felt that the past winter had been but a preparation for such a climax.

Lucia and her mother had been estranged for almost a year now. An uneasiness, of which he felt sure Lucia was totally unaware, had brooded over the household. Many times his wife had spoken of the change in their daughter, but, until to-night, he had been unable to perceive anything but normal physical development. As his retrospection deepened he confessed that until now he had not known his daughter at all. Certainly the child who defended the lady of her vision with such pertinacity was a total stranger to him. He found it hard to believe that she was but ten years old. She had faced the anger of her mother with a respectful equanimity that wavered only under the blows of the woman's hardened palm.

The man winced at the thought. Although he dismissed the possibility of the apparition he was convinced that to Lucia the lady was flesh and blood.

He was roused from his reverie by his wife.

" I really don't know what to do with her."

The man shook his head. What was there to do? For a moment his mind dwelt on the possibility of derangement and instantly shied.

" She's growing up, Mamma." He wished his forced confidences were real. " All children have strange notions at Lucia's age. All this will pass in time . . . in time."

The woman shook her head. " This is nothing new. She has been full of tantrums for more than a year now, dreaming up this wicked story. If the village gets to hear of this—— " She broke off abruptly. Such a contingency was unthinkable. Not all of her neighbours were as gullible as Olimpia Marto, she thought contemptuously. The woman had actually believed the fantastic story of her two children—really believed that they were worthy of a visitation by the Mother of God. What conceit! Well, thanks be to God, she herself had no such presumptuous pride. She must put a stop to it at once, before the blasphemous lie spread to shame them all.

CHAPTER SIX.

THE most notable characteristic of Dòm Agostinho Marques Ferreira was a caution that manifested itself in his slow, deliberate speech and in his habit of long deliberation before committing himself to words. As Pastor of this mountain parish his mannerisms were an essential defence in his fight against the perverted tenets of the Grand Orient at Lisbon, which had invaded even this remote fastness. The civil authorities at Ourem and Santarem knew him as a formidable opponent of their atheistic administration, who contrived by suave diplomacy to obtain the maximum alleviation of the anti-religious laws without appearing to seek it. The peasant parishioners, who came into more intimate contact with the priest, took him for granted. His faded cassock was a familiar part of the scenery. They trusted him implicitly, however, and had an unbounded confidence in his capabilities. Only Dom Agostinho himself knew the frustration that overwhelmed him at times when his role as intermediary between the authorities and his mountain souls grew well-nigh intolerable.

He was experiencing this feeling now as he gazed through his study window and waited for the child to recover herself. Heaven knew he had not meant to frighten her. From the beginning, indeed, he had been determined to preserve an unshakable equanimity, but

42

he was unprepared for such persistent obstinacy. Lucia had clung tenaciously to her story, while offering nothing to substantiate it. He turned around slowly and faced his visitors again.

Of the two, the child was the more composed now. Senhora Santos was so obviously distressed that it was painful to watch her. Yet the priest had found her vigorous support strangely irritating and her constant resort to angry tears unhelpful. He was sorry that he had not interviewed her daughter alone. He looked at the child. Her eyes were swollen and her plain face was pinched and white.

" Tell me, Lucia," he said gently, " did you ever hear of Bernadette Soubirous of Lourdes? "

A mute shake of the head.

" Would you like to hear the story? " The priest seated himself behind his desk. " It is very like the one you told me, only the girl Bernadette was much older than you. She saw the Blessed Virgin, too, and spoke to her, just like you say you did. Are you sure you never heard that story, Lucia? Perhaps somebody told it to you? "

Lucia shook her head again. Her face was hidden, but her fingers fretted nervously with the edge of her shawl.

The Parish Priest heaved a sigh. " My child, I am only trying to help you. I do not say that you are telling deliberate lies, but when we are young fancy plays many tricks on us. You may have only imagined you saw this lady? " It was half a question, but Lucia did not answer, until her mother's voice roused her:

" Lucia, do you hear the good Father speak to you? "

" I saw her," said Lucia. " I did not imagine her."
She spoke without looking up.

Dom Agostinho came to his feet. He felt
exhausted. Perhaps he had not handled the situation
as delicately as he might. But in spite of the negative
impression made upon him by the child's answers, his
natural caution prevented him from making any
judgments. To what extent he wanted to believe in the
visit of the Mother of God to these mountains only he
himself realised. If she had deigned to intervene in
the affairs of oppressed Portugal, then the fate of the
satanic puppets of Lisbon was already sealed. Maybe
he had been too anxious to believe the child's story and
the reaction of disappointment oppressed him.

He spread his hands on the desk. " Do you realise,
child, that you have become the laughing stock of the
village? Can't you see the sorrow and shame you are
bringing on your parents? And, worse still "—he
raised a warning forefinger—" the trouble that will
come from the carabini! Would you like to see your
mother go to jail? " His last question, farily shouted,
startled Lucia. The misery in her tearfilled eyes
instantly softened the pastor. He came around the desk
and laid a hand on the girl's shoulder. She flinched and
immediately burst into tears.

The priest straightened and waved his hand in a
weary gesture of dismissal. " You may take the child
home, senhora," he said, returning to his desk with a
sigh. He had intended to prove Lucia a fraud or a
saint. In fact, he had proved nothing.

His voice halted the visitors at the door.

" When did the lady say she would come again? "

Lucia's face brightened momentarily. " On the thirteenth, Padre."

" Do you know when that is? "

" To-morrow, Padre."

" To-morrow is also the feast of Saint Anthony of Padua. Pray to him, my child, for guidance." For Senhora Santos he had a special word of advice. " God works in many strange ways, senhora, and it is not for us to impede His Will. If this affair is the work of God we will recognise His Hand in time. Meanwhile let Lucia go to the Cova." He crossed the floor and opened the study door. Senhora Santos alone caught his whispered words: " If this thing reappears, bring the child back to me."

In his heart he had a saddening conviction that he would never hear of the mysterious lady again.

*   *   *   *   *

The early morning breeze had a biting sting as it probed at the open shirt of Manuel Pedro Marto. Presently, he knew, it would veer to the west as the sun rose higher to scorch them on the road to Porto-de-Mos. Still, if they hurried, they might, with luck, avoid the noonday heat. Hastily he harnessed the sleepy burro to the cart and led the animal around the house and on to the road. The loose buck-board rattled noisily and he steadied it with his hand—the children were still asleep.

Leaving the cart on the road, he walked quickly to the porch, where his wife awaited him, dressed for the road. A coarse plaited shawl covered her head and passed under her armpits to be fastened in a huge knot at the back. She had a heavy bundle in her hand which he helped her carry to the cart. As they turned towards the house again both of them halted involuntarily. Jacinta stood on the porch watching them.

She was but half dressed and her white face peeped from the long tresses, the eyes still heavy with sleep.

" Where are you going, Mamma? "

Senhora Marto exchanged a glance with her husband.

" We're going to the fair at Porto-de-Mos, you little goose. Go back to bed before you catch cold."

" Then you are not going to the Cova to see the lady? " There was disappointment in the sleepy little voice.

" Well, we must go to the fair, Jacinta. Besides, we didn't think you would be going to the Cova to-day. It is the feast of Saint Anthony. Surely you're not going to miss the romaria in the village? "

Jacinta shook her head. " I'm going to the Cova with Francisco and Lucia to meet the lady."

Senhora Marto lifted her shoulders in a long sigh. " Well, if you insist—but I don't think Lucia will be there. She went to see Dom Agostinho yesterday."

Jacinta understood the implication in her mother's voice. " Lucia will come," she asserted confidently. " She promised the lady she would."

Manuel Pedro, going into the house, tweeked his daughter's cheek. " Saint Anthony's going to be disappointed."

Jacinta took the remark seriously. " But the lady is beautiful, Papa," she called after him, " and she'll be waiting for us." She felt sure that Saint Anthony would understand.

Her mother viewed her with anxious affection. " Tell me, Jacinta, have you heard what the people are saying about your lady? "

The child considered the question gravely and a little furrow formed on her smooth forehead. " They don't believe us, Mamma," she said at length.

Her mother could scarcely repress a smile. " They think you are telling lies, don't they, Jacinta? "

Jacinta nodded solemnly, showing no resentment at this cruder version of her own theory.

" And you know what a lie is, Jacinta? "

" Oh, yes, Mamma."

For the hundredth time Senhora Marto experienced the helpless feeling of complete acquiescence in her daughter's conviction. Every time the child spoke of the mysterious lady, her mother felt oddly reassured of something she had not dared entertain. This imaginative apparition had stood the test of time. Four weeks had elapsed, yet, in spite of ridicule, goodnatured and otherwise, the child's memory and enthusiasm were undimmed. She had become so insistent on the recitation of the Rosary that the beads were now an essential daily devotion for the entire family. Francisco, his unruly ways forgotten, was her devoted disciple, and though a year older, was completely subservient to his sister's will. Both of them were looking forward with such eager anticipation to the lady's advent that

Senhora Marto feared the reaction if she did not come.

" Would you be very disappointed, Jacinta, if the lady didn't appear to-day? "

The child dismissed the question with a naive gesture. " She'll come, Mamma. She said she would, so don't worry."

The woman did worry, but it was not until Fatima was some kilometres behind that she voiced her apprehension.

" Whether she is real or not, I hope the lady won't disappoint them."

Manuel Pedro, seated on the other side of the cart, smiled and tilted his battered hat. " Do you believe there is a lady? " he asked without turning.

His wife glanced swiftly at him and looked away again. " When I'm speaking to Jacinta I never doubt that the lady is real and did come to visit my child. But when I listen to the villagers I'm no longer sure."

Manuel Pedro nodded. " That is just what I feel, but we can do nothing. If the lady is the Blessed Virgin everybody will know in time. For Jacinta's sake I hope that she will come to-day." He flicked his switch over the burro's haunches.

*   *   *   *   *

Even at that very moment the same prayer was echoing in the heart of Antonio dos Santos as he watched the strange procession leaving Aljustrel for Cova da Iria. The humiliation he felt at such publicity fanned his smouldering anger. His big fists knotted, and a pulse beat at his temple as he fought a savage instinct to disperse, by force, the crowd of people who trailed after the three children. He could have sensed their spirit even if they had whispered their mocking innuendoes. As it was, they made no secret of the fact they were undertaking the journey to the Cova to amuse themselves at the expense of three innocent, imaginative children.

Earlier in the day Antonio had decided to go to High Mass and ignore this adventure of his daughter's, but a strong protective instinct now urged him to follow the crowd. Lucia's lady had disrupted the harmony of their household and made himself and his family an object of ridicule, but the child was nevertheless his daughter, and, by heavens! he would see that she came to no harm.

He waited until the people were out of sight. Then, trying to look like any normal peasant out for a stroll on this great Feast-day, he followed them. Kicking at the white dust as he walked, he constructed a hypothetical scene. . . . His daughter and her companions had been talking to their invisible lady when the laughter and jeers of the onlookers had at last broken their extraordinary calm. This was his opportunity. He saw himself walking towards his daughter and facing the crowd. They are surprised to see him. Their mocking insults die on their lips. His words of scorn whip them like scourges and they are ashamed. Some try to slink off unnoticed, but his voice reaches after them, exposing their stealth. They had not expected him to be there. Perhaps they had thought him ashamed of his own flesh and blood . . . ?

Strengthened by the thought of the rôle demanded

of him, he quickened his pace. But the crowd had moved rapidly, and when he caught sight of them again they had reached the Cova. From where he walked he could see that the children were running and had outstripped the straggling people. All had disappeared below the roll of the pasture before Antonio left the road.

At the foot of the declivity he encountered just such a scene as he had previously imagined. Lucia and the Marto children were on their knees near a stunted holm oak tree. The curious crowd had gathered around in a semi-circle. Most of them were squatting on the grass, but a few were kneeling.

As Antonio approached the fringe of the assembly Lucia began to recite the Rosary. Her young voice carried clearly and was answered by the shrill treble of her cousins. A hot surge of mortification dampened Antonio's forehead. Could he blame the people for drawing the natural conclusion that his daughter was mad? And, worse still, that she had perverted her younger companions? Already he could hear the ridicule that must be the sequel to this blasphemous demonstration.

Half way through the first decade the volume of the response grew. Singly and in groups the people changed their positions until all but a few were kneeling. Antonio, scarcely believing his eyes, was the last to conform to the general urge. Stupefaction had held him rigid. He was finding it difficult to believe that the child who was reciting the Rosary with such confidence was his daughter. He was convinced that

Dom Agostinho could do no better, and yet she was but ten years old!

As the prayer ended he saw Lucia come to her feet and face the east. She was perfectly composed and seemed unaware of the watching people. He had often seen her standing thus when he came from the fair at Porto-de-Mos or Ourem, eager and expectant—sure that he had not forgotten her. For a moment he expected the mood of the crowd to change. He sensed its restlessness and started as somebody tittered. Then quite suddenly Lucia gestured towards the sun.

" There! That was a flash of lightning. The lady is coming." She spoke more to her cousins than to the crowd.

Immediately every eye sought the east and recoiled before the blazing glare of the sun. But Antonio had eyes only for his daughter. He saw her kneel, join her hands and stare fixedly at the top of the oak tree. Every shred of colour had drained from her cheeks and even from where he knelt he could see that her forehead was wrinkled in a worried frown. She remained thus for an instant, then suddenly her face cleared in a smile. Antonio had never seen her smile like that before. It was an expression of loving greeting. Now, however, it faded and was replaced by a look of intense concentration, as if she were listening carefully to some speaker invisible to him. Then she spoke herself. Her words were almost inaudible and quite unintelligible, as though she had involuntarily spoken her thoughts aloud. Another pause—the keen concentration again—then another radiant smile.

Jacinta Marto and her brother, kneeling on either side of Lucia, were equally rapt, equally oblivious of the curious gaze of the crowd. The pale oval of Jacinta's face reflected the varying reactions of her cousin, but her brother's features were rigid. His beads were entwined in his fingers, and though his lips did not move, he occasionally allowed a bead to pass between his index finger and thumb.

Antonio dos Santos tore his gaze from the children only when he became convinced that some strange malady had affected his sight, a sudden affliction that tinted the scene a mellow orange. He rubbed his eyes vigorously and opened them again. The scene was unchanged. The three children still kneeling beside the tree were bathed in a soft yellow hue that matched the landscape and the faces of the kneeling people. Close by the wondering man somebody pointed skywards, and there was an immediate chorus of ejaculations. Antonio's eyes followed their gaze and his bead slipped from his nerveless fingers.

The sun which, a moment before, had shone with a blinding glory, now hung like a thin orange wafer in a cloudless sky. On a winter morning, as it rose above the serra, the sun would look like that, but this was high noon. So Antonio reasoned, as he returned his gaze to the children. Lucia had just come to her feet, apparently unaware of the solar phenomenon. She turned to the crowd and for the first time addressed them directly.

" The lady is going now."

As she made the announcement, Antonio thought

he saw a sudden movement of something white at the top of the tree. It seemed as though a bright cloud had risen from the foliage and vanished in the air. So swift had it been that his eyes were hardly focussed before it was gone.

The sigh which, like a sudden breeze, arose from the crowd, proved it no illusion.

CHAPTER SEVEN.

LUCIA was only half conscious of the barrage of questions showered on her. Nor did she feel the impatient hands that tugged at her clothing. The memory of the lady was still fresh in her mind, awakening countless disquieting reproaches. How stupid now seemed her early fears. For a little while before the lightning appeared she had actually begun to doubt whether the lady would come. A deep sense of guilt weighed on her as she wondered if the radiant visitant had guessed her faithlessness. But, if so, she had given no sign; she had been as beautiful and gracious as ever, though the sadness of her expression seemed unrelieved.

Lucia was thrilled at the special intimacy of this second meeting. The lady's remarks had been directed exclusively to her. Occasionally the lovely eyes had rested on the upturned faces of Jacinta and Francisco, but always they returned to her, pleadingly, tenderly, as if she, a poor ignorant peasant girl, had the power to mitigate the suffering of this heavenly creature.

" I want you to learn to read," the lady had said. How this was to be accomplished, and why, she had not explained, but Lucia knew it would be done. The knowledge that she, although but ten years old, was to participate in some Divine plan had so overwhelmed her that she had begged the apparition to take herself and her cousins to heaven—not in years to come when they had completed their allotted span of life—but now while the joy of heaven was burning in their souls.

The lady had smiled at this appeal, not indulgently as adults smile at the extravagant requests of a child, but kindly and sympathetically.

" Yes," she had answered, " I will come soon to take Jacinta and Francisco. But you must remain longer on earth."

Envy of her cousins and a painful sense of loss almost swamped the soul of Lucia before the lady's voice sounded again. " Jesus wishes to use you to make me known and loved. He wishes to spread in the world devotion to my Immaculate Heart."

Even this assurance that her life was to be prolonged only to be dedicated to the service of the Son of God failed to console the child in her bitter disappointment. She could not repress a cry of pain.

" But, senhora, I'll be all alone here."

" No, Lucia, not alone. I will never forsake you. My Immaculate Heart will be your refuge."

As the lady finished speaking Lucia found herself surrounded by a miraculous beam of light which poured from between the parted hands of the apparition. There was a tangible assurance in its warm embrace that completely dispelled the unhappiness in her heart. Through the crystalline light, immediately above the lady's right hand, a strange vision was materialising. Slowly its outline grew until the shape became clear and vivid, emanating a soft glow as of some strange and lovely jewel. Unmistakably it was the image of a human heart whose pulsations laboured against the snare of thorns that wrapped it around and pierced the tender flesh.

The allegorical implication instantly became clear to the kneeling child. Before her very eyes the Immaculate Heart of Mary was being cruelly wounded by the sins of the world. A flood of pity and shame brought the burning tears to the girl's eyes. She had been lonely, envious, afraid, at the prospect of being denied heaven for a few short years. What a trivial cross it seemed now, when she knew that all the time her glorious lady had to bear within her breast a wounded, suffering heart! Lucia strove to impart some of her intense feeling; to tell the lady that she was willing, nay eager, to do anything, though it should mean living on earth a hundred times the normal span of mortal life. But no words could convey her meaning. She found herself mentally repeating the familiar words of the Angelus— " Behold the handmaid of the Lord. Be it done unto me according to Thy word."

*　　　*　　　*　　　*　　　*

Lucia became aware of the questions again. They appeared to grow out of the mental fog that surrounded her.

" What happened? "

" What did you see, Lucia? "

" Did the lady really come? "

She nodded her head at the last question. The vague shadows about her were becoming clearer. She could discern a tight circle of eager, tense faces.

" What did the lady say, Lucia? "

The child thought for a moment. Her heart prompted caution. Instinctively she felt that a revelation of all that had happened would, somehow, be a betrayal of the lady's confidence. Yet she knew that some of it could—no, must—be told.

Somebody tugged at the end of her headkerchief. " Come, Lucia. What did the lady tell you? "

" She asked us to come back on July thirteenth. She also told us to say the Rosary every day."

" Was that all, Lucia? " A peasant woman, with a strained, anxious face, stooped low over the girl. " Surely, child, you didn't forget——? "

Lucia remembered the woman. On the way to the Cova she had asked her to plead for somebody who was sick. Lucia recalled how patiently the heavenly lady had listened to her petition on his behalf. She repeated the apparition's words verbatim :

" He will recover in the course of the year—if he is converted."

The woman jerked herself straight. For an instant a look of anger darkened her eyes, but it was immediately replaced by fear. Hurriedly she made the sign of the cross, then, without a word, elbowed her way through the impatient people.

The questions now began to resolve themselves into a general discussion as to what each of the onlookers had seen. Already everyone was enlarging on the day's happenings. A few, who asserted with vigour that they had heard unintelligible whispers from the top of the tree, had become the hub of an inquisitive group. Others were dilating on the size and brilliance of the

cloud that had appeared to drift from the holm oak.
But inevitably when the personal ego of the individuals
was satisfied the questions were again unleashed on the
three silent children.

" Surely, Lucia, the lady said more than you have
told us? She was there a long time."

The eldest child exchanged a troubled glance with
her companions. Francisco was obviously just as
curious as the impatient crowd, but he had not spoken
a single word, and Jacinta's face, frozen in a deathly
inscrutability, did not help her at all. Lucia turned to
the crowd. It would be safe to divulge one more wish
of the lady.

" She wants me to learn to read."

This revelation was greeted with a gasp of
astonishment. Not two of those present were capable
of reading. They looked at the ten year old child in
wonder. Surely the lady did not expect so young a
girl to accomplish what they, grown men and women,
were unable to do! And even if, by some miracle, the
child did learn to read, what possible purpose could it
serve? This speculation had the effect of so diverting
their curiosity from the main event that they did not
detain the children any longer.

A few people remained behind, among them
Senhor Santos. During the interrogation of his daughter
he had remained, unnoticed, in the background. His
simple, shallow mentality was unable to accept the
possibility of his daughter being honoured by some
supernatural visitation. To him it was as though he
were participating in a wild, uncomfortable dream

from which he would presently awaken, and though he had listened attentively to the speculations of the onlookers he found no measure of comfort in their conversation.

Long after the people, and even the children had disappeared, he moved slowly from the Cova. His hands were thrust deep in his pockets, his chin sunk on his chest. From his state of mental confusion but one clear thought had so far emerged: he did not particularly relish being the father of God's chosen.

*   *   *   *   *

As they reached the village the people from the Cova merged with the throng leaving the little chapel. The news of the second apparition spread like wildfire. The supernatural dimming of the sun had, by now, attained the proportions of a total eclipse; the shining cloud had filled the entire depression: it smelt of sweetest incense. Had the people of the village noticed how the sun went out? No? Then it must have been miraculously confined to the Cova. It had become as dark as night and only for the cloud shining in the darkness they would have been unable to see anything.

A few of the more veracious told the simple truth, and from their account a general consensus of opinion conceded that something extraordinary had undoubtedly taken place. A search was made for the children but they could not be found. Unnoticed they had passed on to Aljustrel.

Senhora Santos came out of the chapel conscious that during the Mass she had not said a single prayer. Between her and the altar had lain the thick cloud of her shame. A month ago she had occupied a position of respect in the district, but now she felt that she had become the centre of open discussion and ridicule. During the Mass she had felt the covert glances of curious eyes drive the hot blood to her cheeks. She was the mother of a girl who suffered from hallucinations—a little mad child who even now had gone to the Cova to bring further shame on her blameless family.

The atmosphere of the little chapel had been suffocating and the Mass seemed endless, but when at length it was over she had remained on her knees. The peaked hood of her shawl was pulled forward over her forehead and her eyes were fixed rigidly on the ground. It was an age before the continual shuffling of feet finally died away, but only then had she risen and hurried to the door, where even the warm afternoon air felt cool on her feverish cheeks.

On the road outside she could see the people talking in groups, and even from where she stood she could hear the babble of their excited conversation. Fervently she hoped that nobody would recognise her. It would be impossible for her to engage in idle gossip or listen unmoved to veiled insinuations, neither could she bear the pity of genuine friends, nor conceal her agitation behind a feigned indifference. She had scarcely taken a step on to the road when she heard her name called. Unheeding, she hurried on, her heart beating wildly. But still the persistent voice followed her.

" Senhora Santos! Senhora Santos! Lucia is back. The lady came again! "

Before the darkness finally clouded her consciousness

Senhora Santos heard somebody scream, and felt the clawing of hands which tried vainly to check her fall into oblivion.

CHAPTER EIGHT.

OLIMPIA Marto drew the threadbare curtains apart, and a broad beam of sunlight slanted across the patchwork quilt of the low bed, touching the chin of Jacinta where it showed just above the light covering. The eyelids of the sleeping girl flickered for a moment and were still again, but a long sigh shook the slender form and she turned on her side.

The woman stood motionless. Jacinta, asleep, made a charming picture. The delicate half circles of her eyelashes showed darkly against the creamy skin which, even in sleep, was devoid of all colour. Both hands were beneath the bedclothes, but the fingers of each were just visible, and, entwined in them, a dark string against the white sheet, was her rosary beads.

As the woman watched, a floor board creaked behind her and Manuel Pedro put his head around the door. Instinctively his wife touched her lips with her forefinger.

" Is she awake? " Only the last word was whispered, and Jacinta puckered her brow and opened her eyes.

" There! " cried Olimpia Marto in exasperation. " You woke her."

" But I thought you intended to? " returned Manuel Pedro puzzled, his voice resuming its normal stentorian tones, now that there was no longer any need for caution.

His wife dismissed him with a gesture and seated herself on the bed. Jacinta was knuckling the sleep from her eyes.

" Did you sleep well, Jacinta? "

The child nodded and yawned. Then, as the full recollection of the previous day's happening flooded her mind, she sat up with a jerk. " Oh, Mamma, you should have come to the Cova yesterday! "

Her mother gripped her tenderly by the arm.

" Jacinta, I want to talk to you about yesterday. What in the world have you and Francisco being doing? The whole village is wild with your story."

The child opened her eyes wide at the gravity of her parent's tone. " We have been doing nothing, Mamma. Only the lady came again, just as she promised."

Olimpia Marto stirred uneasily. Last evening, when she and Manuel Pedro had run the gauntlet of virulent tongues, she had carefully prepared all that must be said to her children. But the sight of the sleeping child had either dulled her memory or weakened her resolve to punish. She felt that if she allowed Jacinta to talk about her lady now she herself would succumb completely to the truth plainly visible in the dark, puzzled eyes.

" Jacinta, you must stop bringing people to the Cova to see this lady of yours." Even as she spoke she realised the absurdity of the implication that a seven year old child could influence adults in such a matter. But, at the moment, she could not think of anything else to say.

" But we didn't *bring* the people to the Cova,

Mamma," the emphasis was marked, " they followed us."

" Did they see the lady, too? "

" I don't think so, Mamma. But she was there. She was just as beautiful as ever." Here the child launched on a vivid description of the apparition. " She was like—— " Jacinta turned her eyes to the ceiling in an effort to find a suitable word to round off her picture. But the comparison eluded her and she allowed her hands to fall on the counterpane. " You should have seen her, Mamma."

Olimpia Marto stared helplessly at her daughter. For some reason she felt perilously near to tears, and the opinions of the village viragoes seemed suddenly very unimportant. She patted her child's head.

" Grown up people are strange creatures, Jacinta. You'll find that many of them don't believe the lady came at all. They will say hurtful things to you, but take no notice of them. I believe in her, child, and so does your father. Now you can get up presently and tell us all she said."

She found Manuel Pedro in the kitchen bending over the fire. He did not even glance at her as she came in.

" Francisco is awake," he announced without turning.

" Did you speak to him? "

Manuel Pedro nodded his head.

" Did he tell you about yesterday? "

Again her husband gave his tacit affirmation.

" Well, what do you think? " asked his wife impatiently.

The man snapped a faggot over his broad knee.

" Woman," he cried, " in God's name! what is a man to think? "

*   *   *   *   *

Neither Jacinta nor Francisco saw Lucia that afternoon although they called twice at her home. On the first occasion, after breakfast, they found the house deserted, with the bleating sheep still in the rickety corral. Some hours later they called again and found Lucia's father smoking moodily on the porch. He looked at them with dull eyes.

" Is Lucia in? " Francisco asked timidly, somewhat daunted by the hard expression on the man's face.

" No, she's not," Senhor Santos replied curtly, and then, as if regretting his tone: " She's gone to Fatima with her mother." He stepped off the porch and pointed the stem of his pipe at the staring children.

" Would you like to know who she's gone to see? " he asked sternly.

The children, suspicious at the tone, both nodded and shook their heads.

" Dom Agostinho wanted to see her about your lady of the Cova. And if you don't stop fooling the people you'll find yourselves before him, too." He gripped his pipe between his teeth, and, hands thrust into his pockets, strode around the gable and left them.

It was almost dusk when the children saw their cousin again. They had been playing listlessly near the end of the field immediately behind their home, when they heard her calling. But they had to search, before locating her in a clump of tall ferns where the two farms adjoined. Lucia's eyes were red and swollen, and the tears had made white furrows down her grimy cheeks.

" Where were you, Lucia? " asked Jacinta. " We looked, and looked, and couldn't find you anywhere. Is it true that your mother took you to Dom Agostinho? "

Lucia nodded miserably.

" Was he angry? " asked Francisco in an awed voice.

Lucia nodded again. The terrifying memory of the priest had started the tears flowing afresh. " He said that the devil was very clever and that he might be using us to fool the people," she sobbed. " He said that the lady might be the devil."

Jacinta was aghast. " But that couldn't be. The devil is ugly—with a long tail—— "

" And two big horns," supplemented Francisco.

" And the lady is beautiful and didn't we see her go up to heaven? " Jacinta finished triumphantly.

Lucia brightened. She wiped the tears from her eyes. " Then you think she couldn't be the devil? " she asked eagerly.

" Of course not." Jacinta's voice showed a certain amount of surprise that her cousin could entertain such a thought.

They had occasion to recall the theory of Dom Agostinho, however, as the thirteenth of the month drew nearer, and the speculative excitement of the people grew. Most of them were frankly incredulous, some flagrantly abusive. Others, influenced by the witnesses of June thirteenth, were inclined to cite Dom Agostinho's theory. Only the people who had actually been present at the second apparition were certain of the sincerity of the three little visionaries, and openly championed them. Meanwhile the children themselves were patiently bearing a subtle persecution. Whenever they appeared in the village they were surrounded by a crowd who annoyed them with questions. Travellers from Ourem, Porto-do-Moz and Leiria, and even from beyond the province of Estremadura, brought home with pride the story of their personal interrogation of the mad children of Fatima.

Only in the privacy of their own home did Jacinta and Francisco find sanctuary. But for Lucia there was no peace, either in the village or in her own house. Her hypersensitive mother had become embittered against her, alternately raging at the family's disgrace, and pleading for a public denial of the supposed apparitions of the lady. So painful had these incessant scenes become that Lucia rarely went to bed with dry eyes. But in spite of this continued persecution, it was only on the eve of the long-awaited thirteenth that a break came in her stout pertinacity.

After supper her mother came in from the village, smarting afresh under the ridicule of the villagers. She reached new heights of abuse in an effort to wreck her daughter's intention to go to the Cova on the following day.

" It's not that I don't want you to go," she said with

forced calmness, " but you know quite well what the good priest said. It might be the devil you see out there. He is a cunning one, child. When he wishes he can make himself as beautiful as a star."

Lucia, seated near the fire, allowed her head to drop on to her hands. Terrifying fears were running riot in her heart. The strain of the past weeks had laid pale fingers across her cheeks and her tearful eyes were deeply encircled with shadows.

" I know you don't want to become a plaything of the devil," continued her mother relentlessly. " Do you, Lucia? "

The child shook her head.

" Then don't go to-morrow, Lucia. There is danger out there for you. You'd be flying in the face of God! "

Lucia raised a tragic face. " I'll have to tell Jacinta and Francisco. They'll be expecting me."

" Then run and tell them, child, before they go to bed. Soon you will forget all this nonsense and be happy like you used to be before the lady came." Senhora Santos longed to fondle the child's tortured face against her breast. The mute misery of the shadowed eyes stabbed her like a knife twisting in her heart.

Lucia was almost breathless when she reached the Marto farm. She found Jacinta and her brother still on the road, but the lamp was already lighting in the house.

" Listen, Jacinta—Francisco," she spoke jerkily, " I'm not going to the Cova to-morrow. If the lady asks for me, tell her I was afraid to come because she

might be the devil." She could hardly bear to watch
the expressions on her cousins' faces, and as she opened
her lips to explain, the scalding tears welled up in her
eyes again. She turned and ran blindly up the road.

She slept but little. A persistent sense of guilt kept
her tossing restlessly all through the long night, but as
the grey dawn lighted the room she dropped into a deep
sleep.

It seemed to her that she awakened almost
immediately, with the sound of her own name in her
ears. She sat bolt upright in bed. Across the room
the big bed, with its tarnished brass knobs, was empty,
and the sun from the open windows made a broad pool
of light on the disordered bedclothes. Prompted by a
desperate urgency, she swung her legs from beneath the
blankets. The music of her name seemed still to linger
in the air about her, like a haunting bar of some exquisite
melody. Quickly she dressed and ran from the room.
In the kitchen she came face to face with her mother.

" I'm going to the Cova, Mamma. The lady will
be waiting."

Senhora Santos, speechless with amazement, made
no attempt to stop her.

A glance at the sun spurred Lucia's feet towards her
cousins' home, but a curious, pervading wretchedness
of spirit weighed her every movement and lengthened
the distance to the Marto farm. It seemed ages before
she found Olimpia Marto standing before the gate.

Lucia paused to catch her breath.

" Have they gone? "

Olimpia Marto smiled at the child tenderly. " No,

Lucia. They are heart-broken. They hadn't the courage to go without you. I'll hurry them now. You haven't much time."

CHAPTER NINE.

IN an agony of remorse Lucia knelt at the foot of the holm oak tree. Goaded by the same imperative urge that drove her from her bed but an hour ago, she had led her cousins and a straggling retinue in a wild dash to the Cova. In the depression were more people than she had even seen at the village romaria, but she had been only vaguely conscious of a number of white staring faces as she pushed impetuously forward; and now, having reached the rendezvous, she had room for no thought other than her own faithlessness to the lady. Perhaps now that her beloved knew how unworthy was the object of her trust she would not come again. The slight breeze drying the perspiration on Lucia's brow was like the cold hand of fear.

Somebody behind her began to recite the Rosary and the girl reached for her beads. Oh, heavenly lady, please come! I really didn't mean what I said about the devil. Send me any suffering as a punishment, but please—let me see you again.

At the last Ave of the fifth decade the lady appeared. But, oh, how changed she was! Beautiful still; resplendent as before, yet the expression of sorrow on her face had deepened, as if she, too, had suffered much since last she had been here. There was pain, as of some deep, secret hurt, in the expressive eyes, and the gentle voice was filled with sadness.

71

" I entreat you to recite the Rosary every day in honour of the Blessed Virgin to obtain the end of the war through her intercession."

The sorrowful inflection of the lady's voice found an echo in the soul of Lucia. Had not she, too, borne the persecution of the derisive villagers, the acrimonious railing of her mother and the crowning torture of her own insidious doubts? If she had but the courage, and if the lady did not look so sad, she would ask her help in convincing the people of the reality of the apparitions. If the vision would but say who she was, and work a great miracle here and now before their very eyes, they would have to believe. The unspoken words tumbled about in the child's mind.

The lady's expression altered slowly. " Continue to come here on the thirteenth of each month. On October thirteenth I shall tell you who I am and I will work a great mircale that will convince all. Meanwhile sacrifice yourselves for sinners and say often, especially when you make sacrifices: ' O, Jesus, it is for love of Thee, for the conversion of sinners and in reparation for the offences committed against the Immaculate Heart of Mary.' "

As she repeated the lady's words, Lucia became suddenly conscious of change. She had a weird sensation of drifting over infinite distances. The lady appeared to be withdrawing from her, as if she stood on some dark, receding shore, but a beam of light coming from her breast reached across the intervening space to the feet of the kneeling girl.

The miraculous ray seemed to pierce the crust of

the earth, pushing it aside with inexorable force, reaching down and down, through dark, fearsome places, through immense cavernous vaults darkened by eternal shadows—down further still, until the pure, clear gold of the piercing light changed to a dark, angry red and dissolved into crimson vapour over a great sea of flame. For limitless leagues on each side, the fire heaved and swelled like an ocean of molten rock, but the deep red glow found no reflection in the pitch black sky.

On the surface of this dread sea floated a terrible flotsam. Human beings in countless millions, writhing in helpless agony, clawed for some tangible support at the air. At times they were indistinguishable from the tongues of fire, but occasionally, as they leaped in torment, the glowing lineaments of their bodies shone a brighter red than the inferno. Among the tortured souls, huge repellant animals, of evil and grotesque shapes, clawed mercilessly, and from all arose a chorus of piteous groans that echoed and re-echoed from the unknown vaults above.

Lucia covered her face with her hands. A stark terror seemed to be crushing the life from her body. She knew that if she looked any more she would die.

" Oh, senhora, for the love of God——! "

She raised entreating eyes. The evil vision had vanished and the lady was over the holm oak tree again. Her lovely face wore an expression of infinite sorrow and the corners of the gracious mouth drooped in pity.

" You have just seen hell, where the souls of poor sinners go. To save them the Lord wishes to establish in the world devotion to my Immaculate Heart. If people do what I shall tell you, many souls will be saved and there will be peace. The war will soon end. But if men do not stop offending the Lord, it will not be long before another and a worse one begins. That will be in the next pontificate."

The sweet voice faltered and the lady looked towards heaven. The wind moving through the Cova stirred the gold embroidered veil and set a gossamer shadow dancing on the smooth cheek.

"When you see the night illuminated by an unknown light, know that it is a great sign that God has given you, indicating that the world, because of its innumerable crimes, will soon be punished by war, famine and persecution. In order to stop it I shall ask for the consecration of the world to my Immaculate Heart as well as Communion of reparation on the first Saturdays of the month. If my requests are granted, Russia will be converted and there will be peace. Otherwise "—the lady's voice sank to a whisper—" her errors will spread throughout the world, leaving a trail of wars and persecution against the Church. Many will be martyred. The Holy Father will have much to suffer. Several nations will be wiped out."

The lady's voice was now scarcely audible, and, as Lucia listened, her own heart beat in slow, deep measure, like the muffled thud of a distant drum. She had caught some of the lady's fear, and its intolerable weight seemed to restrict her breathing. The name Russia was meaningless to her, but she must learn all

about it, since its conversion was so closely linked with
the fate of the world.

" The outlook, therefore, is dark, but there is one
ray of hope." An air of regal authority emanated from
the vision. Her eyes looked challengingly over the
heads of the kneeling people as though meeting the gaze
of an enemy unseen by all but her. " My Immaculate
Heart will finally triumph."

For a long moment the lady stood thus, a stern
figure, then slowly she turned her eyes on the children
and her expression gradually softened.

" Do not tell this to anyone, but you may tell
Francisco. Do not forget to say the Rosary every day
and when you pray say at the end of each decade : ' O,
Jesus, forgive us our sins and lead all souls to heaven,
especially those who have most need of Your mercy.' "

Now for the first time the lady smiled with all her
previous affection, and her gaze swept the three kneeling
children like a loving caress. She inclined her head
slightly, and, with an almost imperceptible motion, rose
from the tree and vanished into the air.

To-day there had been no gradual withdrawal to the
east, just a sudden transition from beauty to drabness
which jarred sharply on Lucia's senses. The world
seemed to be locked in stunned silence. The stunted
holm oak tree looked drab and wilted, the rim of the
Cova bleak and desolate, the grass of the pasture dry
as a bone. Everything in view testified to the great
emptiness of a silent world.

Lucia heard Jacinta exhale a long, quivering sigh.
It was the first sound she had heard since the lady's

departure. Behind, not a whisper broke the stillness. Slowly she came to her feet and turned to the people. Just in front of her knelt her father; she had never seen his lined face so drawn and pale. Near him were the parents of Jacinta and Francisco, the woman openly leaning against her husband's broad chest, his muscular arm supporting her. Beyond were some of the villagers, and people that Lucia had never seen before, all staring in her direction. Perhaps they did not realise yet that the lady was no longer there. Lucia looked at her father and answered the question in his eyes.

" The lady is gone."

* * * * *

Back in Aljustrel Senhora Santos paced interminably about the narrow kitchen. A deathly silence emphasised the metallic measure of the small clock on the mantelpiece. It seemed to boom in the mind of the distraught woman. Listlessly she went to the door and leaned in dejection against the frame. The road outside ran emptily along, skirting an empty landscape bounded by an empty sky. Earlier that morning the air had been filled with the tramping of hundreds of feet all bound for the Cova. The curious glances of the people as they passed the house had been hateful to her. But when the sound died on the road, her relief was short lived. A silence far more intolerable than the tread of wondering pilgrims had descended on the world. No animal moved on the land; no bird flew in the sky; she alone lived among these desolate mountains.

As she turned from the door, a footstep sounded on the hard crown of the road. To her strained ears the step was unmistakable. Furtively she peered out. Her husband was hurrying towards the house, and the urgency of his gait forced her 'out on the road.

While he was yet some distance away he jerked his thumb behind him. " Lucia and the children are coming. The lady was there again."

The wife looked keenly at his perspiring face.

" Are you fool enough to believe that nonsense? "

The man passed in behind her and turned about, brushing the gleaming sweat from his forehead. " The fool I was to blind myself to the truth! God forgive me "—he made a hurried sign of the cross—" But it was because I thought myself unworthy to have a child so blessed by God."

The woman's jaw sagged in astonishment. " What are you saying? You're talking like a fool."

" Perhaps I am. I, and thousands of others, have just seen a miracle."

" You actually saw the lady? "

" No, but she *was* there! " He spread his hands. " How could any normal man doubt it? The sunlight became soft and mellow and round about the tree on which the lady stood was a shining cloud—like the mantle of God Himself. We have been wrong, woman—and cruel and bitter to one of God's chosen."

Senhora Santos was astounded. Such unexpected eloquence was more impressive than all her daughter's stubborness. She had known her husband as a simple, unlettered man, apt to be taciturn except when the warm impetus of wine loosened his tongue. Now, moved by some deep emotion, he was a changed

personality. There was bitter self-reproach in his voice.
He moved to the house and paused.

"The lady told them to say the Rosary every day
to bring about the end of the war. Santa Maria!
Could children who know nothing about such things
invent such a lie?" He shook his head. At the porch
he turned again. "It will come hard to you to believe
the Blessed Virgin came to our child. But if you saw
what I've just seen you'd no longer doubt it. Anyway,
Lucia says that in October the lady will work a great
miracle. Then everybody will have to believe." He
drew his hand slowly across his brow. "Don't scold
Lucia, Mamma. She must be tired. The lady was there
a long time."

He left her standing on the road, bewildered. But
long before the host of praying people came into view
around the bend, the hard bitterness of many months
had melted in uncontrollable tears.

CHAPTER TEN.

THE letter was couched in crisp, official language.
It deplored the " Jesuitical farce " which seemed
to have taken hold of the entire area and, while
exempting the District Administrator from all blame,
stressed the surprise felt at Santarem that Arthuro
d'Oliveira Santos had not suspected the existence of this
plot to overthrow the republican government before it
had attained such dimensions—smoothly overlooking
the fact that the District Administrator and Arthuro
d'Oliveira Santos were one and the same person. The
letter went on to say that the close proximity of
Santarem to Lisbon made it impossible for the writer to
withold the information from the Grand Orient at the
Capital who, in any case, were already in full possession
of the facts and took a serious view of the matter.
In conclusion, the epistle emphasised the need for
prompt action in dealing with the situation and closed
with expressions of confidence, and enquiries as to the
general health of the District Administrator and his
wife. The Prefect's bold signature straddled half the
typed page.

Senhor Arthuro d'Oliveira Santos crumbled the
letter savagely between his fingers. Behind the printed
lines he could almost see the smug, complacent features
of his superior. He would be seated in his comfortable
chair, pressing the finger tips of his podgy hands together

while dictating in that smooth, deep voice which gave little indication of his true opinions. It was all very well for this suave functionary to send sardonic letters when he was not fully conversant with the facts. The importance of this affair of Fatima had grown overnight. True, a whisper 'of the fantastic story had reached the administrative office at Ourem, but who would give credence to any story from mountains already reeking with fable and superstition? What man of intelligence, such as he, Arthuro d'Oliveira Santos, would believe it? It had been a huge joke, pro-government if anything, and he had enjoyed it, until a few weeks ago when he awoke to find the people of his district crying " Miracle ! " Even then he was virtually powerless. One could hardly arrest three very young children because they thought they had seen a mysterious lady. He was convinced that the lady existed only in the imagination of the children. A visit to Dom Agostinho had satisfied him that the Pastor was just as eager to end the matter as the authorities. The enthusiasm of the people was entirely spontaneous; religious fervour was dying hard here in the mountains, which, in the opinion of the Administrator, was perfectly natural, since it is all but impossible to wrest centuries of superstition from the hearts of illiterates.

Taking a general consensus the Fatima supporters were in the minority, and although many were naturally curious, most of them treated the matter as a hoax. The " Jesuitical farce " could still die a natural death if a repetition of these monthly rendezvous were prevented. This the Administrator had every intention of doing,

long before the peremptory letter arrived from
Santarem. It was the irony of fate that the official
communication should arrive at the very hour the
protagonists of the " plot " were due for interrogation.

The Administrator rose from his chair and crossed
to the window. He had carefully formulated his plan
of procedure and his confidence in its success made him
impatient to begin. When the matter was ended he
would show his contempt for the garrulous Prefect in
bypassing Santarem and sending his report direct to
Lisbon. He smiled at the thought. He had youth on
his side, and youth coupled with ambition made an
indomitable combination. Who could tell how far he
would go?

The door opened and his subaltern appeared.

" Senhor," he announced, " the children and their
parents are here."

The Administrator almost smiled at the man.
' Bring them in." He seated himself hurriedly behind
his desk and scribbled industriously on the back of the
Prefect's letter, not looking up until he heard the door
close behind his visitors. He assumed an expression of
surprise.

" Oh, yes! " he said, laying down his pencil, and
pointing a slender finger at the three children lined up
before his desk. " You are the children who are causing
all this trouble? " He raised his eyes to the four adults
for confirmation, but saw only an uneasy exchange of
glances. He returned his gaze to the children.
" Which of you is Lucia? "

Lucia half raised her hand and the Administrator

forced a smile. " I have heard of you, Lucia. You are quite a famous character—and shrewd, too, I'll wager. I'm told that you meet a mysterious lady every month a: "—he consulted a note on his desk—" Cova da Iria. Is that true? "

Lucia nodded. Her face was pale, but her eyes were unflinching.

" You two seem to have quite a chat, Lucia. Can you tell me what the lady says to you? "

Lucia glanced at her companions before answering. " She wishes us to say the Rosary so that the war may end soon."

The Administrator lifted his eyebrows. " That is a very commendable suggestion. Did she say if the war would end in victory for Portugal? "

" No, senhor, she didn't," said Lucia, nonplussed.

Her father ventured to interrupt. " The child knows nothing of such things, senhor. She only repeats what the lady says."

The younger man's eyes blazed at the interference, yet he kept himself under control. " All right, Lucia, I see you are frightened, but there is no need to be. I sent for you because I am your friend and may be able to help you." He leaned forward over the desk. " I hear a lot of talk about a secret the lady confided in you. Secrets lead to a lot of trouble, Lucia, and it's my duty to protect you. Now, do you trust me enough to tell me the secret? "

The child answered immediately. " I cannot, senhor. The lady said we were not to tell anyone."

For the first time the Administrator turned his

attention to the Marto children. "So you know the secret, too. Don't you know that a secret shared is no longer a secret. If all three of you know it, what difference does one more make? I'll send your parents from the room if you wish and then you can tell me. I'll promise to carry it with me to the grave." He looked at Jacinta. "Will you tell me?"

"No, senhor, I can't."

The official's eyes turned on Francisco, but seeing the answer already formed on the boy's lips, passed swiftly to Lucia.

"And what," he threatened, "if I insist on knowing? Do you realise who I am? And what I can do to you?"

Manuel Pedro shuffled a pace forward. "Forgive me, senhor, but they won't tell, even if they die. We, their parents, don't know what the secret is."

The Administrator brought his hand crashing on the desk. "Do you think that I'm a fool? This is no child's fancy. Portugal is at war and here in the mountains we have a lady who talks of ending it. Dark secrets are being whispered not seventy miles from the capital. That is a treasonable offence." He searched the face of Manuel Pedro with burning eyes. "Do you know what treason is, or how it is punished?"

Manuel Pedro stared at the ground. "I have a son, Manuel, who is now at war for Portugal," he said quietly.

The young official took a deep breath. His rising temper was confusing his thoughts. He brushed a hand across his face and when he removed it he was smiling again. "But we are getting excited about nothing. You can keep your secret, Lucia, and I won't put your father and mother in prison—as I could, mind you—if you will do me a favour. It is such a simple thing, and then all this trouble and unpleasantness will be over. Will you promise me now that you will not go to the Cova on the thirteenth? Will you promise that?"

All three children began to answer at once and stopped, then Lucia continued: "We can't promise that, senhor. We must go to the Cova. We would rather die than not go. The lady will be waiting."

"Then let her wait!" thundered the Administrator, all attempts at subterfuge gone. "I'm warning you that if you go to the Cova against my order or continue to poison the minds of the people I'll throw you all into prison." He kicked the chair from beneath him and stood up. "It's waste of time to argue with fanciful children, but you"—his eyes lifted to the scared parents—"I hold you responsible. If you allow the children to continue with this foolishness you will rue the day." The ink-well bounded from the desk. "Now get out, and if you are wise this business will end here."

In his heart, however, he knew he had failed.

A feeling of helplessness depressed him during the next two days—maddening days of frustration and indecision. The Prefect's letter had magnified the gravity of the happenings at Fatima, yet the Administrator could not see in the rustic drama any material threat to the state, but he realised that his prestige, if not his position, was in danger. Until now his career had been meteoric. Since the revolution of 1910, when he had played no small part in driving the hated Dom Manuel from the throne, he had raised himself from Arthuro d'Oliveira Santos, son of the local blacksmith, to Arthuro d'Oliveira, Administrator of Ourem District. Throughout the years his eyes had been fixed on the mecca of Lisbon. An appointment in the capital meant power—power and freedom from the innumerable restrictions on rural authority. It was a dream that had sustained him through the monotonous years in this obscure position.

He could not understand, as he stood at the office window on this morning of August thirteenth, why the prospect of Lisbon seemed to have receded or why his mind had fastened on the sordid memories of the past, rather than on the beckoning promise of the future. He sensed a connection between his mood and the inescapable enigma of Fatima, even now being borne in upon him by the sight of the crowds surging in the streets below. They made no secret of their destination. They had a rendezvous at Cova da Iria with three children and a mythical lady.

As the Administrator watched the oddly assorted stream of humanity flow past, the germ of an idea began to take root in his mind. There would be no stemming the flood of religious fervour if anything happened at the Cova to-day. But if the fanatical, foot sore crowd were to find nothing for their pains, the bubble of this clerical hoax would be finally pricked.

The young official moved swiftly to the door. He

was remembering how the glowing iron was wielded into shape under his father's hammer blows—quick, mighty, decisive.

It took him longer than he anticipated to reach Aljustrel. Hundreds of people and a weird conglomeration of creaking carts jammed the road, and, although it pleased his ego to see them crowd their vehicles into the ditches as soon as they recognised the Administrator's car, he was nevertheless furious at the delay. Two kilometres outside Ourem he reached the head of the procession from the east and drove on at a speed that threatened to rattle his saloon to pieces.

Once at Aljustrel it was impossible to mistake the house he sought. A knot of inquisitive people standing on the road before the gate, scattered at his approach. Lucia, Jacinta, Francisco and their parents were gathered at the porch. They watched him climb out of his car, and as he strode towards them, he was conscious of the respectful silence that had descended suddenly upon the onlookers. He pulled his uniform straight and smiled insincerely at the children.

" I see I'm in time," he said in a conversational tone. " I thought you would have gone by now. It's a pity that you are not taking my advice about not going. But," he smiled magnanimously as the deference changed to alarm in the parents' faces, " I will not jeopardise my reputation for justice and fair treatment, so I have decided to go with you to the Cova to-day and see this mysterious lady for myself."

" You may not see her, senhor," said Lucia quickly.

"I'm sure I will. But what matter—if I see enough

to convince me that somebody is there you shall have no further trouble from me."

The seven anxious faces brightened instantly, and Manuel Pedro grinned nervously. " It is always better, senhor, to see for yourself," he said.

The Administrator looked at his watch. " Isn't it time to go to the Cova? "

" We were just about to go, senhor. The lady comes at noon," Manuel Pedro supplied.

" Good, then you will allow me to drive you there. It's a long walk for such little children."

There was a troubled exchange of glances, then Lucia conveyed the general opinion.

" We usually walk, senhor. The people pray on the way."

The Administrator's smile became fixed as a surge of chagrin almost changed it to a scowl, yet he managed to conceal his disappointment. He realised that recourse to persuasion would be disastrous to his plans.

" As you wish, children," he said almost gaily, his eyes connoting a deep understanding of the eccentricities of the extremely young. " But there is one thing—purely a formality, of course—I would like you to answer some questions in the presence of Dom Agostinho—for my report," he explained hastily, noting the alarm in the children's faces. " I promise I'll keep you no longer than a few minutes. So if you will follow me to the presbytery we will get the nasty business over and you can go to your lady."

He spoke apologetically as if deploring the inconvenience. The deception was so successful that

Senhora Santos urged the hesitant children to comply.

" It will be only for a few minutes, Lucia. We will carry on to the Cova and perhaps the Senhor will drive you over there afterwards."

There was genuine delight in the Administrator's voice. " That is a good plan, senhora, but perhaps it will not be necessary to drive them if they hurry. As you say it will take but a few minutes."

At the presbytery the few minutes extended to thirty while the Administrator compelled the secretly enraged Dom Agostinho to question the children about the lady's " secret." The priest, accustomed to the reticence of the children, knew that no purpose would be served by further cross-examination. Yet caution compelled him to show respect even to this minor functionary. He knew Arthuro d'Oliveira. He was usually officious and overbearing, but to-day his attitude puzzled the priest. The young man seemed to condone Lucia's taciturnity, and by shrewd diplomacy attempted to assume the role of champion of the children against the common clerical enemy. Dom Agostinho was not fooled for long. Nevertheless he was convinced that if the " secret " was not forthcoming, the farcical interview might last all day. To his surprise it was the Administrator who finally terminated the inquisition.

" I'm afraid," he said, studying the dial of his watch, " you will have to let the children go now, senhor. They have an important appointment at the Cova." He smiled at their eager faces. " We will have to drive fast to be on time. It's a great pity, though, that you didn't tell the good priest your secret. He seemed so anxious to know."

Glad that the interview was at an end, Lucia turned to the priest. "If you wish, Padre," she said courteously, " we will ask the lady for permission to tell you, and if she agrees we will come here when we get back."

The Administrator laughed at what he mistook for cunning, but Dom Agostinho was impressed by a wisdom inconsistent with the child's age.

" Do that, my child," he said. "Tell her that I am interested."

    *   *   *   *   *

At the Cova da Iria, under a cloudless sky, the straggling processions from Ieiria, Ourem, Thomar, Santarem and even as far south as Lisbon, had gathered in a compact circle about the tree of the apparitions. Although the majority were openly sceptical, very few were disparaging or hostile and even these instinctively spoke in whispers as if, in spite of their opinions, they were conscious that this barren pasture was holy ground.

In front of the pilgrims and nearest the tree were Senhora Santos and her husband. Beside them were cousin Olimpia Marto and Manuel Pedro. A common anxiety weighed on all four. They had walked slowly from Fatima, allowing the ever-growing crowd to overtake them and expecting at any moment to see their children hurrying from the village. Nearing the Cova, when the children had not put in an appearance, the parents assured themselves that, because of the lateness of the hour, the Administrator would surely bring them in his car. This was but an effort to allay their growing uneasiness, and when at last they reached the depression they would have remained on the outskirts of the crowd had not their neighbours insisted that the parents of God's chosen should have pride of place.

The sun was now nearing its zenith and the anxiety of the four people from Aljustrel was being slowly transmitted to the crowd.

Soon the babble of the assemblage lost its modulated tenor. Impatient questions were levelled at the parents. Those who had witnessed the arrival of the Administrator at the village supplied the uninformed with the story of the children's visit to the presbytery. The explanation had the effect of temporarily assuaging the impatience of the crowd, but at noon, when there was still no sign of the children, the jeers of the sceptical element threatened a mass exodus from the Cova. Some of the people were, in fact, already drifting on to the road when without the slightest warning the sun lost its brilliance, as if a giant translucent hand were suddenly put before its face.

A death-like silence descended on the staring throng. In a sky that had been limpid blue, but was now a vault of deep vermilion, the sun hung like a huge plaque of burnished bronze, emanating a soft orange glow that painted the trees in fantastic shades and gave the pasture a semblance of rich tawny velvet. The wonder of this celestial phenomenon had scarcely penetrated the sensibility of the people, when a white, lambent cloud formed about the tree of the apparition.

For a moment it remained fixed in a semicircular arc, then it dissipated slowly like ascending incense. As if at a signal the sun assumed its normal power.

While awe still held the shaken crowd dumb, a single word reverberated from the fringe of the Cova, and immediately the trance-like immobility of the people was broken. From lip to lip it travelled, first in whispers, growing to loud indignation, and then in sonorous wrath—Kidnapped!

"The children have been kidnapped by Dom Agostinho!"

CHAPTER ELEVEN.

LONG after the sun had sunk behind the high ramparts of Serra d'Estrella and darkness had chased the red streamers from the sky, Lucia dos Santos and her cousins remained by the window of an unfamiliar room. For them the past ten hours had been an incredible nightmare, during which a monster in the shape of the Administrator had threatened and raged while they stood in misery before him. Their arms still ached where the merciless fingers had gripped to shake them in passionate fury. Their eyes were raw and tender from tears that had been their only refuge, although these seemed to goad their tormentor to fresh heights of fury. The children had answered all his questions but one, and it was this last that he wanted most. He tried to make them violate the lady's trust by telling her secret, but so far their fidelity to the heavenly vision had outlasted the young man's tyranny.

There had been short periods of relief when the Administrator had left the room. Only then did they meet with kindness and pity from one who, strangely enough, stirred the same emotions in Lucia's heart. This was a young woman, tall but very thin, with frightened eyes that moved in furtive uneasiness, as though she feared the very shadows. Her voice had been quiet and sympathetic, and once she had offered the children food, which they left untouched. Another time while they waited in terror they had heard her making a passionate appeal on their behalf. When she had re-entered the room a red weal showed darkly on her pale face.

Evening had brought the longest respite the children had known since they came to this house. They had been bundled upstairs and ushered into a bare room filled with the red flush of sunset. An unmade bed in the corner and a low table near the window were all the furniture it contained. Instinctively Lucia and her cousins ran to the window and flattened their cheeks against the cool glass. They had no idea where they were but the outline of the horizon was familiar, although it seemed further away than they had ever seen it.

The Administrator came no more, and as the sun sank lower and lower, and the light in the room gradually died, a loneliness more terrifying than the threats of their tormentor seized the children. Jacinta and Francisco clung to Lucia and she, clasping them tightly, gave a semblance of courage she did not feel. Then, mercifully, as the cold, distant stars filled the sky outside their window, her cousins slept on the floor and left Lucia wide-eyed and aware, a prey to formless terrors. She tried to think of the lady; the glory of her apparel; the beauty of her face; the tenderness of her smile and the wistful sadness of her lovely eyes. Little by little she reconstructed the imperishable image from her memory, until it seemed that the lady stood before her again, then she sank into the sleep of exhaustion.

*   *   *   *   *

A rough hand on her shoulder awakened her. The room was flooded with sunlight and bending over her was the florid face of the Administrator. Francisco and Jacinta were already on their feet.

The man smiled at them sourly. He seemed to have aged overnight.

" So you slept," he said. " That's very good. Have you changed your minds about telling me your secret? " His eyes, shadowed from a sleepless night, searched the three faces and therein found his answer. " All right, little ones, you may keep it for a few hours more, but understand this, I mean to know what your precious lady said. Now get downstairs! "

They did not see him again until after they had eaten some food which the timid woman set before them. She, too, bore the marks of a night without sleep on her haggard face, yet she spoke kindly to them and coaxed them to eat. After they had finished she came over to Jacinta and tenderly stroked the child's hair. Just at this instant, however, the Administrator stamped into the room and his wife snatched her hand away as if the sleek head had become suddenly red hot.

For a long moment the Administrator stood in the doorway, conscious of the tense atmosphere created by his entry. Then he snapped his cane against his shining top boot. The effect was like a pistol shot in the room.

" H'm! You all seem to have eaten your fill. Are you ready now to tell me what I want to know? Very well! You'll soon learn that we have means of making children talk. Come with me."

Mutely the three filed after him into the open air,

but before bundling them into his car the Administrator
had a final word.

" What is about to happen at Ourem is your own
fault. I have been lenient with you—too lenient. I
even gave you your last chance this morning. Now
we shall see who is the stronger, Arthuro d'Oliveira
Santos or your lady of the Cova."

As the car hurtled along the country road Lucia put
her arms about the swaying bodies of her companions.
Jacinta's face, smeared with dried tears, was terrifying
in its pallor. Francisco was as white as his sister and
his mop of hair stood wildly on end. Impulsively his
cousin brushed her hand along the wiry length of it.
She feared for these children more than for herself.
Their presence was an additional torture to her since she
knew their natural frailty as she knew her own tougher
fibre. But their weakness was purely physical and was
more than balanced by a high moral courage. They
would not tell the lady's secret even though they were
to die. Lucia was as sure of their determination in this
respect as she was of her own, and it was rather the
dread of what lay in store for them than any fear of
their infidelity to the lady that gnawed at her heart now.
She had a presentiment that more persecution awaited
them at their destination. The Administrator did not
speak again until he stopped the car in the main street
of Ourem and then it was only to growl a curt
command for them to get out.

At this early hour the town was deserted,
nevertheless there was something furtive in the glance
the official threw up and down the road as he hurried

the children into the Bureau of Administration. Without a word he ushered them into a large room, crowded with chairs laid out in untidy rows before a raised dais on which stood a plain table. He hurried up the passage between the disordered seats.

" Sit down there," he indicated some chairs immediately in front of the table and waited until they had complied with his order. Then he strode to a door adjacent to the dais, but as his hand fell on the knob he turned.

" You need not waste your time trying to escape. All the doors are locked."

The children did not even put his assertion to the test, but sat in silence, frightened and miserable. The building seemed to groan all about them. A breeze rattled the slightly open window above the table. Somewhere outside a clock ticked in a strong, even measure, and occasionally a step sounding in the passage brought their eyes towards the door.

Fully thirty agonizing moments passed before Francisco broke the silence. He had been sitting stiffly with his clasped hands gripped between his knees. Now he shifted his position slightly.

" I wonder what they're going to do with us? "

He was merely echoing the question that occupied the minds of his companions. Nobody offered an answer, but the boy did not seem to expect one. He turned to his sister. " Are you frightened, Jacinta? "

His question won only a mute nod.

At this moment the door opened and the Administrator re-entered the room. But this time he

was not alone; a thickset man, in civilian clothes,
followed him. They seated themselves at the table, and
Lucia knew that the inquisition was about to begin
again. The men held a whispered conversation, then
the newcomer addressed them.

" I am very sorry to see such young children in this
room," he said, apparently with genuine contrition in
his smooth voice. " It is not a nice place. You
see "—he waved his hand in a wide gesture—" this is
where all the bad people come—criminals—before they
are sent to prison, or before they are executed. That is
why I am so sorry to see you little people here and I
know that you do not like it yourselves. Now because
you are so young and so thoughtless I am going to do
my best to get you out of here soon and send you back
to your mothers. You would like that, wouldn't you? "

He smiled expansively as the children nodded.
" Now, before I let you go I want to tell you who I am.
I am the man who sends all the real criminals to prison
so that other people can live in peace. We know you
children are not criminals, but without realising it you
have caused the Administrator and myself a lot of
trouble." He looked at the young man beside him
almost with compassion.

" I am quite sure you did not mean to do this, and
I do not blame you half as much as the people who
follow you. It pleases you, doesn't it, to be the centre
of attraction and to think that all these foolish people
believe in your lady? But "—he stroked his heavy
chin—" you know as well as we do that there is no
such person—— "

"But there is, senhor," interrupted Lucia, almost before she realised it. "There really is."

The Administrator moved impatiently, but his companion laid a restraining hand on his arm.

"Well, you surprise me, Lucia," continued the magistrate smoothly. "And I believe you. Could you tell me what kind of a lady she is? Is she Portuguese?"

"I don't think so, senhor," Lucia answered readily. "She told us she came from heaven."

"And you believe her?"

"Oh, yes, senhor. She couldn't come from any other place. Besides, we saw her go up there."

"To heaven?"

"Yes, senhor. We all saw her." Francisco and Jacinta nodded in vigorous agreement.

"There doesn't seem to be any doubt about it, does there?" The older man seemed impressed. "Now, if you tell me what the lady says, you can go home to your mothers. It's getting late and you will be wanting your dinner." He consulted a watch on his thick wrist.

Eagerly Lucia related all the lady had told them, omitting only that which, under no circumstances, could be revealed. Here and there in her narrative Jacinta corroborated with enthusiastic affirmatives.

When the eldest child finished speaking, there was another whispered conference at the table. The Administrator was obviously irritated and inclined to argue, but the suave voice of his companion, reaching the children as a deep murmur, eventually pacified him.

"I'm afraid you disappoint me, Lucia," deplored the

thickset man. "I thought you trusted me sufficiently to tell me all the truth."

"But I have told you the truth," said Lucia.

"Come now, child. There is something you have not told me and that is the very thing that is causing all this trouble. Did not the lady tell you something else? Something that you have not told us yet?"

All through the interrogation Lucia had dreaded that the questions would revert to the secret, although the amiable voice of her interlocutor had somewhat lulled her fears.

"I'm sorry, senhor," she said with genuine contrition. "I'd tell you if I could. But it's a secret. We cannot tell anybody."

"That is a great pity," murmured the big man. "You place me in a very awkward position. I do not like to hurt little children, but we must know this thing you are trying to hide. Tell me—is your secret good or bad?"

Lucia thought for a moment.

"For some it's good and for others it's bad."

"In what way is it bad?"

"I cannot tell you, senhor."

"But I must know, Lucia," insisted the big man, gently. "Do you understand that? You will be sent to prison and you will never see your parents again unless you tell me."

In the silence that followed Jacinta began to sob quietly.

"I'd like to tell you, senhor," cried Lucia brokenly. "But I can't—we promised—we promised."

This time the restraining hand of the magistrate failed to keep the Administrator in his chair.

" Then you'll die! All of you. You'll be fried in oil. Do you hear me? Roasted alive! " He struggled against his companion's restraining hold. " Let me alone. There is but one thing these mountain brats understand."

He strode savagely to the door and his angry orders rang through the building.

The man at the table gazed curiously at the weeping children.

CHAPTER TWELVE.

PABLO Ladron looked at his cell mate with unconcealed contempt, then moved restlessly away again. He was indignant. High functionaries of the carbonari, police and prosecutors, had all, at one time or another, expressed their appreciation of his sparkling humour. Magistrates of four provinces had been charmed by his outspoken audacity and on occasions had relented to such a degree as to allow a note of regret to creep into the stereotyped sentence. Pablo had come to expect such respect from everybody, for though he was a thief he was perhaps the best thief in all Portugal, worthy of respect either in court or in prison, and certainly entitled to a better habitation than this infested dungeon, unfit for pigs. He had said as much in the last hour not only to this ragged individual who brooded in his filthy blankets as if the name Pablo Ladron meant nothing to him, but also to the armed guard who lounged in the corridor outside the bars. Both men had apparently remained unimpressed, but the garrulous youth was neither silenced nor discouraged.

" I tell you, my friend," he said, leaning against the barred door, " this is the worst jail I have ever been in. It is unfit for pigs—or have I told you that already? Never mind, it is still so. Now in Leiria they have a prison of tolerable dimensions, with two windows, worthy of fellows of my calibre, and the food—come to think of it that was not so good—but it is wine and spices compared with the slop of this fleabitten cow shed." The guard, chewing on a wad of tobacco, remained impervious to the flood of eloquence.

" Say what you like, my friend," said Pablo, returning to his taciturn cell mate, " Ourem can pride itself in having the worst jail in all Portugal. I believed that one in Porto was bad, but this "—he spread his hands and paced across to the man on the bed—" where in the world would you get another like it? "

His companion allowed his back to slump further down the stone wall. " Santa Maria, amigo, will you not let a man rest? "

" There you have it! " exclaimed Ladron derisively. " Where can a man rest? I tell you there has been no rest in all Portugal since the good Dom Manuel was robbed of his throne."

The jaws of the guard paused and a sudden light gleamed for an instant in his beady eyes.

" The country," said Pablo, ostensibly to his disgruntled fellow prisoner, " is riddled with cringing despots who wage war on priests and nuns for paltry sums that can never buy them the freedom they want most." He caught the beady eyes of the guard. " I am a prisoner here, yet some day I will go, but not you, my friend, you are here eternally—a prisoner outside the bars."

The gaoler crossed slowly to the bars. Only the rattle of the keys on the ring he carried betrayed his agitation. Before he had taken two paces there was a commotion at the end of the corridor and as he glanced in that direction his jaws gaped, revealing the tobacco balanced on a blackened tongue.

Pablo Ladron craned his neck against the bars but could not see the object of the guard's surprise until, after some hurried and subdued conversation, two more uniformed men came into view escorting three weeping, unresisting children.

" Caspita! " swore Pablo Ladron. " Don't tell me that they lock up children in Ourem." He turned to his cell mate. " Here is something, amigo, that will knock you from your stupor. In what other country in the world is this done? "

The ragged individual had indeed roused himself sufficiently to stare in amazement as the door was opened and the three children propelled into the cell.

After the heavy key had turned in the lock Pablo strolled to the bars. " Brave fellows," he complimented the three guards. " What courage we have here in these mountains. You have rounded up some very dangerous criminals—enemies of state, no doubt. You will, perhaps, get a medal for this? "

Undecidedly they stared at him for a moment. Then, as the mocking gaze brought the blood to their faces, the two newcomers stamped away and the guard reverted to his tobacco.

Pablo Ladron urged the children to sit on the hard bed.

" Don't cry, little ones. You have, no doubt, murdered our good Civil Administrator? "

The boy shook his head in surprise. " No, senhor, we have not."

"A pity," murmured Pablo. He looked at the children with genuine compassion. "Tell me. What are your names?"

"I am Francisco Marto, and this is my sister, Jacinta. She is Lucia."

"But who else could you be!" exclaimed the youth. "I have heard of you. Who in the whole of Portugal has not?" He touched the sleepy man with his boot. "Do you see who we have with us, my friend? The little ones to whom the Holy Virgin appeared." He gazed at them in mock wonder. "You are saints, chicos, and this is no place for saints—only for such as our sleepy friend here. How do you come to finish in prison when you should be in a convent?"

"It's because of the lady's secret, senhor," said Lucia, trying to keep back her tears. "The Senhor Administrator wants to know what it is and we can't tell him because the lady told us not to."

Uncontrollable sobs began to rack the thin body of Jacinta. "And now we are going to be fried in oil and we'll never see our parents again."

As Pablo Ladron watched in helpless sympathy, Francisco put a comforting arm about his sister's heaving shoulders. "Don't cry, Jacinta. Remember what the lady said. We can offer this for the conversion of sinners. Remember Jacinta—'Oh, Jesus, it's for love of Thee and for the conversion of sinners.'"

The little girl's terrible sobbing ceased and she looked at the earnest face of her brother through tear-filled eyes. She brushed her disordered hair from her face. "And also for the Holy Father," she said unsteadily, " and for the sins committed against the Immaculate Heart of Mary."

Pablo Ladron crossed to his former position at the bars and cleared his throat. Fiercely he blinked a mist from his eyes, half ashamed to have softened so much. A week ago he had laughed uproariously at the story of three foolish children who had created a panic in the Portuguese press. His anarchical spirit had exulted in this fresh governmental embarrassment. He had propagated the story, elaborating it in his inimitable way and enjoying the effect on his hearers. Now he was face to face with the protagonists of the mountain drama and he was finding the experience wholly disturbing. His easy scepticism had suddenly died. These were no ordinary children. What youngsters of their age carried such suffering on their faces, or spoke with such familiarity of things that rose like accusing spectres before his mind—Sinners—The Immaculate Heart of Mary—The Holy Father?

In an effort to recapture some of his lost exuberance he rattled the door violently.

" Did I tell you, friend, that this is a lousy prison? " he enquired of the indolent guard. " Well, let me add that your Administrator is also a—— "

A hand tugging at his jacket interrupted him. Jacinta was at his side and was holding something out to him.

" Will you hang this on that nail, please? " She indicated a nail that protruded from the wall two metres from the flagged floor.

As Pablo took the medal from her he felt the hot

blood rush to his face. Hurriedly, with one eye on the grinning guard, he hung the medal on the nail, and, ignoring the child's thanks, returned to the bars glaring. Even as he searched his mind for colourful phrases, the children began to recite the Rosary. The subdued voices completely shattered his train of thought. He felt his mind slipping back through the years, to the time when the words of the children were as familiar as his present lurid vocabulary.

After the first decade he turned around. The children were kneeling in a row facing the wall where the medal caught the reflection of the sun. Near the bed the other prisoner had come to his knees, and, elbows on the blankets, held his head between his hands. Almost furtively, Pablo Ladron tip-toed from the door and sank to the floor behind the children.

*   *   *   *   *

The sun streaming through the small, barred window had made a complete semicircle of the cell before the Administrator came. Pablo Ladron, dozing quietly in the corner, first became aware of the presence of the functionary when the peremptory voice grated on the ears.

" Well, have you made up your minds? Are any of you going to tell me? Very well! You "—he snatched at Jacinta's arm—" you will be the first to die." He beckoned to the two guards who stood, shamefaced, beside the barred door. " Take her away ! "

Without a backward glance the child delivered herself unresistingly into the hands of the guards.

Lucia and Francisco watched her go in silence, and only
when the heavy lock turned again did a groan of anguish
escape the white lips of the boy. Instinctively he buried
his head on the shoulder of his cousin.

In the thirty minutes which followed, Pablo
reached fresh maledictory heights. He stormed across
the floor in a helpless passion. Occasionally he paused
by the children and murmured awkward words of
comfort, but, seeing the resignation on the thin, tragic
faces, he stalked to the bars and cursed the guard with
such hearty ferocity that the latter forgot his tobacco
for once and a look of apprehension clouded his eyes.
By the time the Administrator returned Pablo was
hoarse.

The expression on the young official's face as he
stepped into the cell was of deepest sorrow.

" Jacinta," he said, spreading his hands, " is dead.
She was so foolishly obstinate. I hope that you'll have
more sense. It's not pleasant for me to kill little
children. I appeal to you, Lucia. You can save this
boy's life and your own, if you'll tell me what the lady
said, or admit publicly that there is no such person."

Lucia's groan of anguish was quite plain, but so
was the negative shake of her head.

" Then, I'll take the boy now."

Before he quitted the cell, Francisco managed a
timorous smile over his shoulder. But in his eyes was
the stark terror of death.

When they had gone Pablo Ladron became
reflective. What was he after all but a loud mouthed,
useless thief, who railed at the police but shrank from

committing himself in the presence of the
Administrator. When it came to his turn to die some
day, let him go like that young boy whose smile had
fought so bravely to mask his horror.

The cell was almost dark when the Administrator
came back. This time he paused outside the locked
door and spoke through the bars.

" Lucia, you are the only one left. Jacinta and
Francisco are dead. I won't come in for you if you'll
tell me your secret. It is such a little thing to have cost
the lives of your two little friends."

" I cannot tell you, senhor," said Lucia quietly.

The Administrator turned to his companions.
" Get her out of there." In his voice was the weariness
of abject frustration.

An hour later, when the last vestige of light had
faded before the encroaching darkness, Pablo Ladron
spoke from where he sat huddled in the corner.

" Sinners. . . . . The Holy Father. . . . . The
Immaculate Heart of Mary."

CHAPTER THIRTEEN.

DOM Agostinho had lost favour with his flock, but he had not realised to what extent until he stood watching them pour from the portals of the chapel. Although the majority saluted him respectfully, there was a cold reserve in their salutation that hurt. It was not pleasant to be disliked. Yet, considering the nature of their suspicions, he could scarcely blame the people. They believed him responsible for the disappearance of the children, and therefore considered that he had betrayed both his vocation and their trust in him by acting as an auxiliary government official. He recalled the angry mob that had surged about his house two days ago. They had not dared lay hands on him, but he knew that it was fear of sacrilege rather than any personal loyalty that had restrained them. It had been his first experience with an angry mob and he had not liked its raw savagery. He could still see the hatred in their eyes and hear the piteous pleading of Senhora Santos and Senhora Marto as they knelt in the dusk and besought him to give them back their children. He winced now at the memory. At first he had quietly and categorically denied the charges, but finally his rising temper had thrown caution to the wind, and he had raged at them with Latin fury. His vocation was to the ministry and protection of the people, not to the kidnapping of imaginative children who had been

109

goaded to insanity by the gullibility of sensationalists!
He did not know where the children were. They had
left with the Administrator, and he for one did not wish
to see them again!

He regretted his words immediately afterwards,
although they had driven the unconvinced mob from
his doorstep. It was untrue to say that he did not care
what became of the children. They were members of
his wild flock, and had not the Good Shepherd left the
ninety-nine to search for the one that was lost? He
was vitally concerned in their welfare, and that evening
his anxiety drove him to the Bureau of Administration
at Ourem.

The Administrator was not there; neither were the
children. The surly official knew nothing of his
superior officer's activities nor of the whereabouts of
the missing cousins. If they were lost so much the
better. This Fatima business was driving everybody
crazy!

On his return Dom Agostinho called at the
children's homes and found them full of consoling
neighbours. The young ones had not returned.
Quietly he told them that he was beginning to fear they
had been arrested. The parents had listened in
respectful silence. Only Olimpia Marto had blurted
out : " Wherever they are, Padre, their lady of the
Cova will protect them."

That had been two days ago and on this morning of
the Feast of the Assumption he resolved to make
another visit to Ourem. This time he would not move
until he had seen the Administrator. If necessary he

would go to Lisbon. One thing was certain, he would
not return without the children!

Dejectedly he moved across to the presbytery. His
housekeeper held the door open for him before he
reached it, her face grey with fear.

" What is the matter? " he asked in alarm.

" The Administrator, Padre—he was here."

" Was here! " The priest swung round on his heel
and swept the road with fierce eyes. " How long is he
gone? "

" He came during the High Mass. He brought the
children."

Dom Agostinho swept the housekeeper aside and
half ran to the sitting-room. As he burst open the door
three haggard children rose from the couch. The
suffering they had endured was clearly marked on their
faces. A great rage against the insolent functionary
swelled in the priest's heart. He had difficulty in
keeping his voice calm.

" What happened to you children? Where were
you? "

" The Senhor Administrator took us to prison."
There was a tremor in Lucia's voice. " He wanted to
know the lady's secret. But we didn't tell him even
though he was going to kill us."

Dom Agostinho clenched his hands. If the
Administrator had only waited he might have forgotten
his priestly calling. The important thing now,
however, was to get these children to their homes. He
ran to the door and jerked it open. A few moments
before, he had seen Senhora Santos and her cousins leave

the chapel.   They could not have gone far.   Actually
they had not moved at all.   From where the priest stood,
he could see that they formed part of a group in the
centre of the road.

He had to call twice before he succeeded in
attracting their attention.   When at last they looked
in his direction no further explanation was necessary,
for the children ran past him and scurried wildly
towards their parents.

For a moment Dom Agostinho watched the tearful
re-union.   He felt as though a great weight had lifted
from his heart.   Even the bunched fist viciously shaken
at him from the excited group failed to mitigate his
happiness.   No doubt this incident afforded further
proof of his complicity.   But, perhaps, the children
would explain.

      *   *   *   *   *

In the late afternoon Lucia and her cousins went to
Cova da Iria.   They slipped away quietly, escaping
with relief from the incessant host of visitors who
crowded their respective homes.   In many ways the
day had been as arduous as the preceding one.   The
enquiries of the people, though friendly and
sympathetic, taxed their endurance and Lucia's throat
was sore from endless reiteration of her experience at
Ourem.   She told them simply of her detention without
stressing unduly the harsh treatment of the
Administrator.   But of her own secret sorrow she said
no word.

One of the first things she learned on her release
was of the beautiful cloud that had enveloped the tree

on the thirteenth. The lady had come and neither
Francisco, Jacinta nor herself had been there. Of
course, the lady might not have known of their
abduction and perhaps had thought—was thinking even
now—that they had deliberately disappointed her.
Lucia imagined the beautiful visitor waiting patiently
over the holm oak tree as she scanned the kneeling
throng for three familiar faces to give her welcome.

With heavy hearts the three children hurried along
the road. They did not know if the lady were free to
come at any time. Perhaps she had other missions to
perform and had but set aside the thirteenth of every
month to come to Fatima. Any deviation from that
arrangement might upset her plans, but there was a
chance, however slight, that she might come to-day just
to hear why they could not keep their last appointment.

Secretive as the children had been they could not
conceal their destination, and when eventually they
reached the Cova about two score people were following
them. Lucia and her cousins knelt before the holm oak
tree and began to recite the Rosary. Since last they
had been here somebody had erected a makeshift altar.
Long, thick withes were thrust into the ground and
bent to form an arc over a plain timber table. This
latter was covered by a white strip of linen, soiled now,
on which were placed two candlesticks and four vases
of flowers. Beneath the table and at the foot of the
tree was a collection representing nearly every
denomination of Portuguese coin. They lay in an
untidy heap, offering a constant distraction to Lucia's
prayer. Those foolish people! Did they not know

that money was worthless to the lady? The copper and silver coins seemed to the child to be a monstrous insult, as if the lady were a beggar soliciting alms. She hoped her beloved would understand that the people meant no disrespect. The makeshift altar, too, seemed a paltry homage to so gracious a personage. The contrast between the glorious vesture of the lady and the crumpled linen decked with wilted blooms, was so poignant that Lucia felt near to tears. The very leaves of the holm oak tree seemed to droop in dejection, and the landscape appeared to be painted in drab, hopeless colours that emphasised the growing conviction in Lucia's heart: The lady would not come to-day. Perhaps she was hurt by their absence on the thirteenth, and now, insulted by the mendicant offerings at the foot of the tree, she had decided to come no more.

Spiritless, the children finished the Rosary and at one accord, as if each had the same conviction that the lady would not come, they moved from the Cova.

*   *   *   *   *

Francisco Marto had in many respects a greater depth of feeling than his cousin or sister. Since he had learned from Lucia that he would go to heaven if he said many Rosaries he had developed an intense devotion to the prayer. His beads were rarely out of his hands, but since he would not display his piety he usually fingered them in his trousers pocket. At first it pleased him to keep account of the number of times he had recited the Rosary since June, but eventually the numbers were too great for him. The Rosary had become a habit. Invariably he offered the prayer as a petition for sinners, but during the following days his sole intention was for a re-union with the lady. Unlike Lucia and Jacinta he had never heard her speak. But occasionally when she turned her seraphic eyes in his direction the boy would thrill to their gentle compassion. Of late he thought that the lady looked more often in his direction, and, it seemed, with deepening tenderness and affection, as if his constant repetition of her prayer had broken the barrier that had lain between them. The possibility that she would not come again filled him with horror. So he prayed, not to make up the deficiency in Rosaries necessary to enter heaven, but that the lady would come again and smile with the sweetness that filled his eyes with tears of remorse.

Four days after their disappointing visit to the Cova, he was out on the pasture of Valinhos behind the village of Fatima. He stood there in the sunshine, absently watching the scattered sheep. One hand grasped his stout hazel staff, while the other, buried deeply in his pocket, moved lovingly over his beads, as he sent his new petition winging heavenwards. A little distance away Lucia and Jacinta sitting on the grass were idly stringing flowers in a slender chain. Quite near, the steeple of the chapel rose from behind a high bluff but the rest of the village was hidden. A brooding quietness had settled on the afternoon, and although a breeze tempered the August heat it moved noiselessly over the pasture.

Earlier that morning Francisco had watched the entire population of the village, headed by Dom Agostinho, leave for the Divine Office at a neighbouring village. The boy had never seen Fatima so deserted.

Not a single person was to be seen in the streets as he and the girls had moved through to the pasture, and the bleating of untended sheep sounded forlornly from the deserted houses. The same loneliness prevailed here on Valinhos and as he prayed a certain sadness weighed his spirit.

Then, in the stillness of the afternoon, he heard his name called. The syllables fell on his ears like three exquisite notes of music. Instantly he turned. The sight of Lucia and Jacinta suddenly falling to their knees occasioned no surprise. Immediately discarding his staff he hurried to them and just before he knelt beside them he saw the lady.

The singing of his heart was almost stilled by the tragic expression on her face, and the sadness of her eyes, as they met his for a fleeting second, drained the smile of welcome from his face. He heard Lucia speak and saw the lady's lips move in reply. Dumbly he delved in his pocket and pulled out his beads. His petition this time was for the alleviation of the lady's suffering.

Some measure of consolation was offered for the ensuing moments, in which he appeared to be forgotten, by a radiant smile of gratitude which the lady turned on him before she disappeared.

Two days later, while Fatima still rocked with the news of the lady's return, Lucia went voluntarily to the presbytery. Although her heart beat with apprehension she forced herself to lift the heavy knocker. The loud metallic clatter almost sent her scurrying away, but the door was opened at once by the housekeeper. The elderly woman scowled at the child who stood, so obviously ill at ease, on the doorstep.

" What do you want? "

Before Lucia could answer, the big frame of Dom Agostinho appeared behind the housekeeper. He looked for a moment at the child, appeared to hesitate, and then beckoned with his hand. Timidly Lucia followed him into the sitting-room. The priest indicated a leather upholstered chair and she sat on the edge of it.

" So! " Dom Agostinho seated himself opposite her. " To what do I owe the honour of this visit? Is it in connection with the return of your lady? "

Lucia nodded assent. " Yes, Padre. It's about the money."

" What money? "

" The money that the people are leaving at the Cova."

Dom Agostinho slapped his knee impatiently. " Is there any end to their madness? Well, what about it? Do you want it? "

Lucia shrank back in horror. " Oh, no, Padre—I asked the lady what we were to do with it."

Dom Agostinho leaned forward in interest. " And she said—— "

" That two processional biers were to be bought." Lucia spoke slowly, trying to repeat the words of the lady verbatim. " One is to be carried by myself and Jacinta with two other girls, all of us dressed in white, and the other by Francisco and three other boys, also in white. On the biers Our Lady of the Rosary must be borne in procession and paid great honour."

The priest stared in astonishment at the child's intense face. He had expected something very different. But the speech appeared to have been carefully rehearsed.

" Who told you to say this, Lucia? "

" The lady, Padre."

" Nobody else? "

Lucia shook her head, the old fear dawning in her eyes.

Dom Agostinho sighed deeply. " Lucia, I really do not know what to say to you. You're either a very imaginative child or a very wicked person. You saw the trouble you brought on yourself and your cousins by persisting in this nonsense of the lady. If you don't stop the Administrator will come after you again."

" The lady was very angry with the Senhor Administrator," Lucia said involuntarily.

" Was she now? No doubt she would be. Did she say how she was going to punish him? "

" No, Padre. But she said that on account of what he did the miracle will be less magnificent."

Dom Agostinho, who had deliberately closed his ears to all talk of the apparitions, felt his temper rising.

" Is there any bound to your madness, child? What miracle? "

" The miracle the lady promised for October thirteenth. She said it would convince all."

The priest ran his fingers through his hair. He could not understand why he should feel so angry.

The unfortunate child was obviously unbalanced and but for the effect she had on the people he would feel nothing but sympathy. He determined to close the interview before his annoyance took the upper hand.

"Your lady really will have to work a miracle to convince me, Lucia. Now, if you are quite finished? I have many things to do and I am sure that you are anxious to get back to your lady."

Eagerly the child left the chair and somehow her obvious relief irritated the priest. He knew she was afraid of him. During their conversation she had kept twisting a pleat of her skirt into a thousand creases. Yet she had come here apparently on her own initiative to impart the lady's wishes. At the door he detained her for a moment.

"Do you really believe the lady is the Blessed Virgin, Lucia?"

Lucia became thoughtful. "She never said so."

"But do you believe she is?"

The child's deliberation was longer this time. "Sometimes I think she is."

"Now, Lucia," said the priest directly, laying his hand on her shoulder. "Do you really think that the Blessed Virgin would come down from heaven to tell you what to do with a few discarded escudos?"

"Oh, no," Lucia answered at once. "She came to remind us of September thirteenth and to ask us to make sacrifices for sinners."

Dom Agostinho looked at her, searchingly. He found it difficult to believe that this child was only ten years old. She spoke with deep sincerity. Why then was he unable to accept that which he wanted most to believe? Perhaps this mental turmoil softened the hard lines in his face, for when Lucia spoke again her voice was confident and friendly.

" The lady said that many souls are lost because there is nobody to pray or make sacrifices for them."

Dom Agostinho let her go. He closed the door and with an unaccountable feeling of weariness re-entered the sitting-room. Beside the window and half in the shadow of the heavy curtain was a picture of Our Lady of Dolours. The priest looked at it earnestly for a full minute, almost without realising what he did.

There was an urgent appeal in his eyes—an appeal he could not frame in words.

CHAPTER FOURTEEN.

THE man from Lisbon swung the car a little to the right and waited with an impatient foot resting lightly on the clutch while a pair of oxen pulled a lumbering cart over the cobble stones. Then, in low gear he allowed the car to glide to the kerb and climbed out stiffly.

He had always remembered Ourem as a sleepy town where time had little market value, yet to-day the streets seemed to have thrown off their customary lethargy and donned the activity of a fair day. The sidewalks were thronged with people who overflowed on to the road and coursed between every imaginable type of vehicle.

The man from Lisbon, strolling up the sidewalk, found himself jostled from side to side. Women bearing prodigious loads of merchandise on their heads and walking with incomparable grace, swept him from time to time on to the road. Fidalgoes, gipsies, Jews, carriers, peasants and yelling children, speaking in a hundred different dialects, merged as so many currents into one strong tide of humanity, flowing through the streets. By the time the stranger reached the Bureau of Administration his hat was askew and his tie crooked. In the dark hallway, festooned with an untidy litter of pinned notices, he made the necessary adjustments to his apparel and presented his card to the sleepy official

121

who yawned and disappeared with it down the
corridor. The heavy footsteps tramping up the stairs
echoed in the silent building.

He was gone but a few minutes when he returned;
there was a new respect in his bearing.

" The Administrator will be delighted to see you,
Senhor Almeida."

The Administrator was indeed delighted to see such
a famous visitor. He met him at the door of his office
with outstretched hand.

" Well, Senhor Almeida, this is indeed a pleasure.
I have long been an admirer of your work."

Senhor Avelino d'Almeida nodded his appreciation
of the compliment and shook the proffered hand.

" May I say," gushed the Administrator, seating
his visitor in a chair, " that from your pen comes the
only vestige of sanity that remains in Portugal." He
jerked his hand to the window. " The people, as you
may have noticed, have gone crazy."

" I did notice quite a lot of excitement," agreed the
visitor, " like a market day."

" Only it isn't a market day," said the
Administrator. " Overnight we have suddenly
developed a floating population of several thousands.
Every square centimetre of accommodation has been
taken. And do you know why all this prosperity has
suddenly descended on Ourem? It's because to-morrow
is the thirteenth of September. The day on which the
mysterious lady comes to Cova da Iria." He sat down
at the desk. " Could you ever have thought, senhor,
that in this twentieth century, people would believe such

a fantastic story? No doubt," he added hastily, " you
have come in a purely journalistic capacity. I have
read your works in 'O Seculo' and 'Illustraçao
Portuguesa,' and believe me, senhor, they have been my
only consolation. A few more articles along the same
lines and Fatima will become the laughing stock of
Portugal."

The journalist inclined his head. " I am glad you
think my work helps."

" Helps! " repeated the Administrator. " Indeed
it does. Though unfortunately the majority of the
people in my district cannot read. Nobody knows,
senhor, what I have to endure. From Santarem I get
letters "—he ran a lean finger through the papers that
littered his desk—" demanding an end of this madness.
But the Prefect does not appreciate the difficulties.
What can I do? Can I take a detachment of soldiers
and arrest a lady who does not exist? Can I arrest the
children—who must be the most stubborn in the world?
Besides, I alone am aware of the mood of the people.
It has become hostile to law and order. To prevent this
to-morrow I would need a regiment of troops."

" It's clear that you are in a very difficult position,'
agreed the journalist sympathetically, " and I am sure
no man could have done more than you to prevent this
cult from reaching its present proportions."

The Administrator beamed on his visitor. " It's
so refreshing to talk to someone who understands. As
you say, I have tried everything. Twice I interviewed
the children and on the last occasion I thought to terrify

them into telling me the truth by threatening to fry them in oil."

The journalist crossed his legs. " Of course, they denied the whole story at once? "

" Unfortunately, no." Arthuro d'Oliveira Santos heaved a sigh. " They are suffering from some hallucination, and they cling to their story with the tenacity of the insane. Could one ever hope to get satisfaction from them? But wouldn't you think that such a fright would bring them to their senses? Not at all! Four days later they said the lady came to Valinhos. She will, probably, appear at the Grand Orient in Lisbon before she is done."

The journalist shared in the official's laughter.

" Prior to this, of course, she always appeared at Cova da Iria. Is that true? "

" Yes," answered the Administrator. " There was, however, a good reason why she should choose Valinhos that day."

" Indeed? "

" You see I had planned a little entertainment for the people on the same date—a little counter-demonstration at Cova da Iria."

" Very shrewd," commended Avelino d'Almeida.

Senhor Arthuro d'Oliveira Santos nodded. He did not feel called upon to tell of the abortive effect of a counter-demonstration in the deserted village nor of his own angry frustration on that occasion. The prospect of his name and loyal efforts appearing in the columns of " O Seculo " was too bright to be dimmed by further talk of failure.

" You are a sympathetic listener, Senhor Almeida."
He smiled expansively. " And I hope I have given you
a true perspective of affairs in Ourem."

" Indeed, you have," the journalist assured him.
" But my main purpose in seeing you was to investigate
a rumour of a promised miracle on October thirteenth.
Lisbon is alive with it. I wonder if you know anything
of the matter."

The · Administrator frowned. " It's a mere
fabrication on the part of these children. The lady is
supposed to work a great miracle in October. That's
all I know. But it may turn out for the best, because
if nothing happens—and, of course, nothing can
possibly happen—it will end this affair once and for all.
I wouldn't envy those brats then. A people who are
capable of believing in their story to this extent are
capable of tearing them to pieces when it has been
proved false. You have my permission to print that if
you wish," he finished hopefully.

Avelino d'Almeida hid his smile.

" You seriously think there will be riots? "

" Nothing," said Arthuro d'Oliveira emphatically,
" short of a miracle will prevent it. You'll see the
tenor of the mob for yourself at the Cova to-morrow.
They are like people hypnotised."

The journalist rose from his chair. " Unfortunately,
senhor, I will be unable to attend to-morrow. But I
shall endeavour to be at the Cova for the miracle.
That should prove amusing at least."

The Administrator saw him to the door.

" Believe me, Senhor Almeida, your entertainment is assured."

            *   *   *   *   *

A little less than twenty-four hours after the visitor had steered his car from Ourem, Lucia dos Santos, Jacinta and Francisco Marto, together with their respective parents, arrived at Cova da Iria. It lacked a few minutes to noon. Already the amphitheatre was thronged with thousands of people, and along the road a continuous stream of pilgrims was crowding into the depression. The sight of such a vast gathering sent a thrill of apprehension through Senhora Santos, but with unfeigned calm Lucia and her cousins passed through the way which was cleared for them.

The outward appearance of the eldest child gave no hint of the joy that filled her heart. The days since the lady appeared at Valinhos had dragged with heartbreaking slowness, but she had tried to appease her longing by increased devotion to the Rosary. Each time she recited the prayer the memory of the lady brightened and the moment of her promised advent seemed to come appreciably closer, until now the poignant waiting was at an end and the lady was about to come.

Before she knelt on the grass Lucia turned to the people. She half raised her beads.

" You must pray," she said.

Starting from immediately before her a great wave of movement seemed to pass through the Cova as the vast assembly went on their knees. Scarcely had it subsided when the sun, radiant on this September day, slowly began to lose its power. It was as though the hand of God had turned down the lamp of the world, and one by one, as the gloom thickened, the stars appeared in the blue vault of the sky, shining like distant candles. Not a whisper broke the stillness of the watching people. Lucia herself could scarcely breathe, and her heart beat violently. Once she looked at her companions. Jacinta's eyes were ardent in the supernatural twilight, but Francisco knelt as if graven from stone, only his lips moved and occasionally the string of beads quivered as he moved them through his fingers. Lucia was waiting for the lightning flash which was the lady's usual harbinger, and as a light suddenly appeared in the east, the child straightened expectantly. But this light was constant, glowing with a steady brightness in the shrouded sky, moving gradually towards the west. It grew larger as it approached, a globe of lambent gold.

Only now was the hush of the crowd broken. The voice of a child shrilled—"Look, there she is! The lady is coming! " Here and there in the crowd the cry was repeated, but after that first thrilling ejaculation, Lucia lost consciousness of all outside distraction, for every fibre of her being was absorbed in mute contemplation of the beautiful lady of the Cova.

From her position behind the kneeling children Senhora Santos watched her daughter with anxious eyes. She saw the plain face suddenly pale as if irradiated by some unseen light. The eyes were staring unwaveringly upwards; no flicker disturbed the intensity of their gaze. Only once did the child move and that was to hold up her hand towards the tree. Grasped in the white fingers was something that glittered. The hand remained extended for an instant and then was swiftly withdrawn as Lucia thrust the object away in her pocket.

Senhora Santos could not hear what her daughter was saying. The child spoke in whispers and then only very occasionally. Most of the time she appeared to be listening. Now and again she would nod her head, but never once did her posture lose its strange rigidity. Only when the light of the sun began to brighten did the child relax. She half turned her head and caught her mother's eye.

"If you want to see the lady—look in that direction."

The eyes of those nearest the tree followed Lucia's pointed finger. Senhora Santos stared fixedly into the brightening sky but could see nothing only a blue void from which the stars were beginning to disappear. Yet even before these twinkling points of light vanished in the growing radiance of the sun, the air was suddenly filled with descending rose petals. They floated down from the sky like great flakes of snow filling the depression with their exotic perfume. Senhora Santos cupped her hands to collect some of the petals, but even before they reached her eager fingers they vanished completely. Nor did they cover the ground as she expected, but dissolved and disappeared before they reached the trampled grass, as if unmeant for contact with the earth.

As the sun reverted to its normal strength the celestial shower thinned and died leaving the air sweet and fragrant.

As usual an enquiry was held immediately the children came to their feet. Lucia had learned to anticipate the interrogation. She told them the lady had again insisted on the recitation of the Rosary in order to put an end to the war.

" Did she say anything else, Lucia? "

" Yes," Lucia answered eagerly. " She promised again that she would work a great miracle and that Saint Joseph and the Child Jesus would come also, and that Our Lord would bless the people."

Lucia's news was repeated in excited whispers. On the morrow, carried by the thirty thousand witnesses, the news of to-day's message would be scattered even beyond the frontiers of Portugal.

On the road home Senhora Santos broached the question that was uppermost in her mind.

" Lucia, what did I see you raise in your hand? "

The child flushed, then took a little bottle from the folds of her skirt.

" A child gave me this to give to the lady."

Her mother unscrewed the small stopper and sniffed at the contents. It was Eau-de-Cologne.

" Wouldn't the lady take it? "

" No," answered Lucia. " She looked at it for a moment and then she said: ' That is not needed in heaven.' "

CHAPTER FIFTEEN.

JOAQUIM dos Santos lifted the bundle of faggots from the mud and slung it easily across his broad shoulders. Gently he pulled on the raw-hide cord until the awkward load rested between his shoulder blades, then doubling the thong twice around his broad, hardened palm, he faced down the narrow, muddy road. Beneath him at the foot of the gentle declivity the houses of Arnal seemed to huddle together under the lowering sky, and their air of dejection in a wet world was in harmony with his present mood.

He had been out but an hour. Of late he dared not go far from the little white cabin that housed himself and his wife, not since the day when, after six hours of toil, he had returned to find her collapsed on the floor yet making pathetic efforts to reach her chair. On that occasion he had finally admitted to himself that his wife was dying; that all hopes of her recapturing her strong, vigorous beauty were dead, and something within him had died, too. For six years he had been nursing the conviction that once again she would be as on the day when he first carried her across the threshold of his home. Even the slow but merciless emaciation of her frame through the years had failed to shatter his faith in a final cure. But now he knew beyond all hope that she was doomed.

His only comfort was that he had done everything

possible for her. Their present impoverished condition
was directly due to the titanic effort he had made to
preserve that spark of beloved life. And as a testimony
of his endeavour had she not outlived the doctor's
prediction? A fortnight, he had said, and that had
been more than two months ago. But then all doctors
were fools. Was it not on their advice that he had
taken her to Batalha for what was to be a certain cure?
How enthusiastic Maria had been, and he, with hope
rekindled, had encouraged her. He had regretted his
optimism later when they had come back, bowed by the
reaction of failure.

She had grown steadily worse. A tick of the clock
seemed to bring a new shadow to her face, a week
developed another complication. Her racking cough
grew harder and lasted longer until it seemed that it
would shatter the fragile frame. Then there was the
pain that had no particular location but ran like fire over
her body until her anguish was as a knife in his own
heart. Only her courage sustained him. It shone like
an unfailing beacon from her eyes. It manifested itself
in the smile that masked a blinding agony and under its
benign influence he had not spared himself.

Since hope of her recovery had died he had prayed
for her deliverance. Yet he had never wished that she
would die in order that he himself might be freed from
her gentle burden; not even in the last three months
when suffering had killed every vestige of the beauty he
had once known. It was pathetic to watch how she
sought to hide her swollen hands and feet which formed
a terrible contrast to the frail form. He blamed himself

bitterly for not being able to hide his own heartache but
her distress was too apparent to make a pretence of
cheerfulness possible.

Now he was praying that she would die. Perhaps
even now, as he was nearing the house, she was dead—
lying on the floor, perhaps, as he had found her before,
only this time, terribly still. A sudden dread seized him
and he splashed blindly along the road.

She was smiling as he burst in, but his wild
expression made her quickly grave.

" What is the matter, Joaquim? "

He recovered himself instantly, and eased the
faggots from his shoulder.

" Nothing, Maria, but fear of the rain. It will
begin again soon." He crossed to the fire and poked the
dead ashes. The perspiration of fear was still wet on
his palms.

In silence he set the fire, glad of the loud crack of
the faggots as he snapped them across his knee. But
before he had filled the blackened grate his wife spoke.

" Joaquim, do you believe I am going to die? "

He turned to her in feigned amazement. " Such a
thought, Maria——! "

" Don't be afraid to tell me the truth, Joaquim," she
interrupted gently, " because I know myself that unless
a miracle happens I will die very soon. That is why I
am going to Fatima to-night."

" Fatima! " He echoed the word that had been
on everybody's lips for the past month. Preoccupied
with his own miseries, he had given scant attention to
the extraordinary story, but he had been grateful for it

supplying his wife with a fresh interest. He had never suspected that she believed it.

" I have promised the Blessed Virgin that I will go barefooted to Cova da Iria four times if she will cure me," said his wife, as he stared at her in astonishment. " And to-morrow is the 13th of October, the day on which she promised to work a great miracle. All the village people are going."

Her husband spoke almost gruffly. " But even if I permitted this madness, how will we go? We have no money for a car and the Cova is all of twenty-eight kilometres."

" We will walk, Joaquim. I have promised the Holy Virgin that I will walk all the way."

The man turned to the fire and snapped a faggot savagely across his knee. " It is impossible. You'd be dead before we reached the Cova." He snapped his teeth on the last sentence. He had not meant to be so brutal.

" Do you think that if I don't go I will live? " asked his wife quietly.

Normally he would have been ready with an instant avowal, but something in the weak voice asked for the truth.

" Do you, Joaquim? "

In agony he stared at the unlit fire and the silence grew tense. At last he turned.

" When do you think we should start? "

  * * * * *

An hour after midnight, they left the house. The rain, threatening all the afternoon, had begun to fall

after dark and now was pouring from a pitch black sky
in relentless sheets. It danced in rivulets on each side
of the dark road; it roared among the leaves of an
occasional tree; but it fell noiselessly on the poor
protection of Maria do Carmo.

The entire evening had been spent in preparation
for what was to Joaquim a foolhardy journey. He had
wrapped some food in a coarse bag and augmented his
wife's apparel with a closely-woven blanket. For
himself he had not troubled, and it was she who insisted
that he drape another blanket about his shoulders.
But, even so, he knew that their clothing was
inadequate. A sense of utter hopelessness enveloped
him as he supported his wife.

She walked slowly and her weight bore heavily on
his arm. She was strangely quiet and his alarm at this
only subsided when he felt the rosary beads entwined
among her swollen fingers. No doubt she was praying
for the strength to sustain her through twenty-eight
kilometres and perhaps half as many hours.

At some distance from Arnal, where the road joined
the highway, they became aware of another sound
besides the falling rain—the tread of many feet plodding
in the mud. The stream of humanity flowing past them
seemed endless, and the soft murmur of many voices
was reassuring. Involuntarily he pressed his wife closer
and looked down at the pale beloved face. Even in the
darkness her eyes had not lost their inspiring lustre.

They stopped often and allowed the procession of
pilgrims to pass them while she regained her failing
strength and he rubbed the blood into his cramped arm.

He kept his thoughts from dwelling on her naked feet. If she had felt the cold of the wet road or the sharp prick of a stone, she had given no sign, and he had not added to her suffering by betraying his concern.

Towards the dawn, the stops had become more frequent. A deadly weariness, more mental than physical, seemed to have drained him of energy. He marvelled at his wife's endurance. It was always she who decided to push on, always she who marked another kilometre off the long journey. Once in desperation he had entreated her to turn back.

" If I do, Joaquim, I will go back to die," she had said, and he urged her no more.

To him, it was a dismal, hopeless dawn. The strong wind had died, but the rain still prevailed. The landscape was grey and desolate, and the clouds seemed just above their heads. Behind them and in front were sodden groups of people, trudging with dogged tenacity in the direction of Fatima. Joaquim was conscious of their curious and sympathetic regard as they passed, and for once he felt no resentment. His first glimpse of his wife's face after the long, weary night had shaken him to the core. It was as though he supported a corpse. Her sunken cheeks, already deathly, had become grey, and long wisps of hair that had escaped from beneath her soaked shawl were plastered to her shrunken face. No trace of colour was in her lips, and the swollen hands which still fingered the rosary beads were blue with the cold. He dared not look at her feet. She did not flinch from his gaze, and while he stared at her in undisguised dismay she had said : " You

are tired, Joaquim. It has been a long night for you."
No word of herself, and for once he was glad of the
rain on his face that so effectively concealed his tears.

As the light strengthened, the cars began to appear
on the road. Every imaginable kind of vehicle
overtook them—automobiles crowding the pilgrims to
the ditches and deluging them with mud, creaking carts
jolting a score of dripping scarecrows, carriages swaying
on their springs and trundling along to the lively
hoof-beats of the streaming horses. At every road
junction the numbers swelled until the road was jammed
from ditch to ditch. As they drew nearer to the place
of the apparitions, the atmosphere of pilgrimage
intensified. Some were reciting the Rosary aloud,
others began to sing hymns as the tempo of religious
fervour grew. A few, like Maria do Carmo, were too
exhausted to do more than pray in silence and allow
themselves to be borne along in the throng.

Joaquim and his wife reached the Cova scarcely
thirty minutes before noon. More than eleven weary
hours lay behind them but the sight of the vast assembly
that crowded the depression temporarily heartened
them. Never had they seen so many people. Dark,
gleaming clusters of umbrellas here and there broke the
uniformity of the sea of faces. Whatever Joaquim dos
Santos thought of his wife for believing in the promised
miracle, it was clear that the mysterious lady of the
Cova had tens of thousands of other followers in
Portugal. Shoulder to shoulder they rose on tiers from
the gaudily decked holm oak; plebian and aristocrat;
soldier and civilian; young and old; man, woman and

child; every degree of society, sex and creed; the curious, the sceptical and the fervent; all stood ankle deep in mud and waited.

From where he stood on the high ground at the fringe of the crowd, Joaquim could see the improvised altar built near the tree. Two unlighted candles stood between vases of flowers, and among the low foliage of the tree little patches of colour showed against the dark green. There was something depressing about the garish decorations—a touch of the incongruous that struck a sceptical note in the man's mind.

A low murmur of excitement heralded the arrival of the children. Joaquim could see where the crowd surged back to allow them through. Those about him lifted themselves on tip toes and craned their necks. When the movement subsided, he saw that the three children had approached the improvised altar and were kneeling in the mud. Near them were some adults, apparently privileged, since they were allowed inside the clearing before the tree. There followed a moment's silence. Save for the persistent patter of rain on the umbrellas, not a sound came from the closely packed people. Then, starting as a whisper and swelling in volume like the sound of a rising wind, came the responses to the Rosary.

Instantly umbrellas were furled and at one accord everybody knelt on the sodden turf. Joaquim dos Santos spread his wet blanket on the ground and gently assisted his wife to her knees. He himself bent a stiff leg to the ground and the earth stung coldly through the drenched material of his trousers. He was conscious, as he automatically muttered the responses, of his wife's voice. She was praying fervently with eyes fast shut and the crucifix of her beads trailed in the mud. He wished he could do something to ease her discomfort, but he could think of nothing except to place his shoulder where she could lean against it.

The rain stopped before the Rosary ended and Joaquim reflected that if the prayer had not brought the lady it had at least effected this small mercy. The sky, however, was leaden still, and he did not doubt that the dry spell would be of short duration. He could see by the expression on his wife's face that she had attributed the ordering of the elements to supernatural intervention and he smiled at her in agreement. Then a vivid flash of lightning swept beneath the dark clouds and he looked at her no more.

The atmosphere had become suddenly pregnant. He sensed that something extraordinary had happened below. Although he was too far away to see any expression on the children's faces, he was aware of a marked tenseness in their attitude. The stillness about him became deathly. Then, even as he watched, he saw a shimmering cloud of vapour, like an embodied light, form about the tree. Scarcely believing his eyes, he looked at his wife for confirmation. Her face seemed ablaze and in her eyes was a joy he had never seen before.

" Do you see the cloud, Maria? "

Her rapid glance was reproving. " I am sure the Holy Virgin is here," she said.

Some of her enthusiasm was transmitted to the

kneeling man in the thrilling moments that followed. The cloud was no illusion. It formed a luminous crescent about the foliage which suddenly turned to vapourised gold as a shaft of unexpected sunlight pierced the clouds.

In amazement Joaquim gazed skywards. A moment before the sky had appeared impenetrable, now the sun was pouring its light through a rent in the dark ceiling.

It was Maria who called his attention from this elemental wonder. He felt her trembling violently against his shoulder and looked down at her in alarm.

" My hands, Joaquim! " Her whisper was hardly audible. She held them out for him to see.

The blue, swollen fingers of a few minutes before were now almost natural in colour, and the swelling had visibly lessened. But the change did not end there. In the sunken cheeks was a flush of blood, the first he had seen there for five years. The whole face, in spite of its emaciation, was animated and healthy and all signs of weariness which had shadowed it had vanished.

" Maria," he whispered. " You don't think——? "

But his wife was not listening. She was bowed almost to the ground and Joaquim could not tell whether she was praying or weeping.

The first miracle had happened—at Fatima.

CHAPTER SIXTEEN.

TO-DAY the lady seemed more beautiful than ever, radiating a hitherto unknown degree of graciousness and glory. Even the habitual sadness of her expression seemed less intense on this great day, when she was about to reveal her identity and work a miracle to convince everybody. Lucia's heart responded to the heavenly lustre of her lady in a fresh triumph of love and she fell into an immediate ecstasy.

For the three children it had been a trying month. Only the night had been their own. They had been repeatedly and incessantly bombarded with questions. Every time they appeared out of doors they were surrounded by curious people, while their homes were constantly invaded by strangers who came with inexhaustible supplies of questions and countless petitions. Priests and laity alike had considered it their due prerogative to seek information of the lady. Not all of these visitors had been polite. Three men had come to Lucia's home and created a frightening scene, with wild talk of death and imprisonment. " How good that would be," Jacinta had exclaimed to the amazement of all present. " We love Jesus and the Blessed Virgin so much; we shall go to Them more quickly." There had been rumours of a plot to blow up the tree of the apparitions, and although the children heard it without fear, their parents had been frightened to such a degree

as to suggest sending them away from Fatima for a time.
The suggestion was firmly opposed by the children and
vigorously denounced by the population, some of whom
had prospered in catering for the constant influx of
visitors. Finally Lucia's mother had suggested
confession, as a preparation for any event.

"If you wish to go to confession, Mamma, I shall
go with you willingly," Lucia replied calmly, "but I
have not the slightest fear." Her words were an
indication of the unshakable serenity that had enveloped
her as the promised day approached. All the previous
visits of her lady had been only a preparation for this
culminating revelation. Soon the lady would say who
she was and the great miracle would end the doubts
and persecution for ever. The child did not doubt that
after the thirteenth all scepticism would end, and from
Fatima, devotion to the Rosary would spread
throughout the entire earth, then the lady would no
longer be sad.

Only as she knelt before the holm oak tree was
Lucia's happiness momentarily clouded. She had been
indifferent to the falling rain, but the decorations of the
altar depressed her. Pathetic wisps of coloured silk,
wound among the branches of the tree, hung limp and
soaking. She longed to reach up and pull them down
lest they desecrate the feet of the lady. The cloth on
the altar was saturated and the two candles had long
been extinguished. Even the blooms in the vases had
shed some of their petals, which now stood out on the
wet cloth like stains.

But the lady had not found any disrespect in the

garish decorations. On the contrary, she had placed her feet on the few strips of bunting that were entwined among the topmost branches, as if in approval of these humble offerings, and instantly Lucia's dread was allayed.

For a long time she feasted her eyes on her beautiful lady. Neither seemed in a hurry to break the ecstatic moment by speech. The lady simply stood with her hands joined, as on all previous occasions, and allowed her blue, seraphic eyes to dwell on the three upturned faces. But, slowly, born of the prompting that was forever latent in her mind, Lucia spoke.

" Senhora, who are you? "

The lady smiled at her as if she had expected the question. For a moment her lovely eyes lifted to the vast assembly, as if acknowledging the huge numbers that had come to-day to hear the wondrous answer. Then she returned her gaze to Lucia.

" I am Our Lady of the Rosary."

At last the final, irrefutable admission. This glorious Visitant was indeed the Mother of God. Lucia's happiness was unbounded. All through the five preceding months, in spite of the prompting of her heart, she had been in doubt as to the actual identity of the Lady, who, she argued, could be but some high angelic messenger, like the Angel of Peace. But now she was sure—now she could refer to the Lady of the Cova as the Holy Virgin without hesitation or fear. She longed to know if Jacinta and Francisco had heard the words of the Lady, but, fearful of breaking even a

moment of this ecstatic union, she fought down the
impulse to look at her cousins.

" I want a chapel built here in my honour,"
continued the Lady. " The Rosary must be recited
every day. The war "—for a moment a shadow seemed
to fall on Her face—" will end soon and the soldiers
will return to their homes."

Requests for the safe return of absent sons and
husbands had formed a large percentage of the petitions
which had been showered on Lucia. She made an
effort to recall them all, yet wondered if the
presentation of such a long list might offend the Lady.

" I have so many favours to ask you, Senhora," she
began apologetically.

" I will grant them to some people," said the Lady
immediately, " but not to all. Jesus does not trust
them." The sweet mouth drooped at the corners and
the familiar look of intense sorrow crept over her face.
" Men must no longer offend our Divine Lord," she
entreated, " Who is already offended too much."

There was a note of finality in the sad voice and
to Lucia's deep regret the shimmering outline of the
Lady began to fade. Every fibre of the child's being
seemed to be voicing a poignant appeal. " Please,
please, Senhora, stay a little longer." The Lady smiled
and opened Her hands releasing a beam of light that
swept upwards towards the sky.

Startled, Lucia jerked her head upwards and an
involuntary cry escaped her. " Look at the sun! "

The Lady was in the sky on the right of a sun that
resembled a plaque of dull silver. Her raiment had

changed. Instead of the gold embroidered veil, a blue
cloak fell on each side of her white robe. On the other
side of the sun was Saint Joseph dressed in red and in
his arms was a Baby Whose hand was raised in
benediction. The tableau lasted only an instant, but
scarcely had the picture vanished when Our Lord
appeared, this time as a grown man. Lucia felt her
heart pounding wildly, for she knew that this was He
of Whom the Lady spoke. She recalled the urgent
appeal : " Men must no longer offend. Our Divine
Lord." Lucia felt a passionate desire to declare her
fidelity, but before she could frame her thoughts, the
Lady appeared again, standing beside the majestic
Figure. Her garb was again blue and white, but the
very folds of her mantle wrapped closely about her
shoulders seemed to emphasise the intensity of Her
sorrow. Many years were to pass before Lucia
associated the image with Our Lady of the Seven
Dolours. The last apparition was of Our Lady dressed
in the vesture of Carmel, a scapular hanging from Her
fingers. For a long moment the Vision appeared beside
the silver sun, then it melted as vapour into the blue
sky, leaving a painful emptiness in Lucia's heart.

CHAPTER SEVENTEEN.

FOR the first time in his life Avelino d'Almeida was afraid. And his fear was so absolute that he no longer sought to conceal his shaking hands, nor cared if those about him could see his agitation. He was remembering with chagrin the gloating satisfaction he had felt when he read his own scathing article in the columns of " O Seculo " that morning. It had been, in his opinion, a masterpiece of satire—a death blow to the superstitious farce of Fatima. He had written it with calculated subtlety, warmly condoning the " correct " attitude of the clergy with a suave sarcasm that left no doubt as to their complicity in this reactionary Popish plot. The work had then seemed worth the long hours of careful composition, and it was in a mood of complacency that he had motored to Cova da Iria on this Saturday morning.

His mission was purely journalistic. In his own mind he was convinced that every word he had written was the absolute truth. Nothing but the urge to gauge the true dimensions of this mass hysteria had prompted him to come to Fatima. On Monday morning his reactions would appear in his usual column of the morning paper, to the detriment of the imaginary Lady who was adding to Portugal's shame. And to-day Portugal, seething in anarchy and disruption, needed every effort to pull her from the quagmire of corruption.

145

She was the " lame dog " of Europe, with a floating
debt of two milliards of escudo; small wonder, Avelino
d'Almeida had reflected, since she was honeycombed
with rival Bolshevist cells that had already bred sixteen
revolutions, eight presidents and more than forty
changes of ministry in sixteen years. Politically the
country was corrupt, financially it was beggared, and
now the seeds of a seventeenth revolution were being
sown by a malicious invention of the clergy.

But the enemies of Portugal had reckoned without
Avelino d'Almeida. This battle against ignorance,
gullibility and cunning had become a personal
challenge—his pen dripped with satirical venom
against the wiles of the priests.

He had not been prepared either for the number
or the character of the crowd that he found gathered
in the muddy depression. His astonishment was
equalled only by his outraged alarm, for this bizarre
expedition, worthy of the scorn of all enlightened
humans, was not attended by peasants alone. Among
them, gaping with all the credulity of the lowest
goat-herds, were the best brains of Portugal. Nobility
and aristocracy rubbed shoulders with the peasants, as
if the latter were their social equals, and in many cases,
yielded to an excitement that filled the journalist with
contemptuous rage. Roundly he had cursed their
stupidity in encouraging this farce by their presence.
And while he waited in the rain he mentally constructed
the caustic comments which would be his printed
revenge.

But that had been more than fifteen minutes ago.

Now all his thoughts had turned on himself, because for once in his well-ordered life he was face to face with the inexplicable.

His scepticism had outlived the vapour which had formed about the holm oak tree. He had longed to push his way through those sixty thousand people and pull the rustic altar to pieces to reveal the hidden burners which he felt sure the crude boards concealed. He had, in fact, resolved to carry the plan into effect, when, at what appeared to be a command of one of the children, everybody looked skywards. Reluctantly he followed their example. For a moment he stared in stunned amazement, before slowly dropping to his knees.

The sun, glimpsed through a gigantic rent in the curtain of cloud, had become transformed into a gleaming, well-defined plaque as of polished silver, emanating a soft white glow that threw the drab landscape into grey relief. It defied comparison with any familiar solar body, as if some hitherto unknown planet had suddenly approached the earth. To the journalist it seemed like the eye of the Eternal Deity irresistibly searching his soul. Then even as he gazed at it fearfully, the mysterious body began to revolve; slowly at first, with a barely perceptible motion, but gradually increasing to such a dizzy speed that the momentum of the spinning orb was lost in what appeared to be a dazzling immobility. This phenomenon lasted but a moment before the whole world seemed to burst into flames. A blood red streamer flew from the flying disc. Immediately it was augmented by another ray, this time of exquisite indigo, and another and yet another, until every colour in the spectrum was flashing in a gorgeous coruscation across the sky. Colours of unearthly tint and beauty chased each other from the clouds to the earth with a bewildering rapidity that defied the senses to descry any definite pattern. The celestial spectacle lasted for a few minutes, then, as the whirling orb slowed to a stop, the beams gradually died, leaving the vast amphitheatre bathed in eerie grey light.

Still in the grip of awed silence, the people stared breathlessly skywards. As yet they were unable to grasp the magnitude of what was happening, and a feeble searching of their minds produced no comment. The children had promised them a miracle, it was true, but this prodigy was beyond the bounds of their intellect—too stupendous to be feasible. But before their bewilderment could loosen their tongues the sun began its multi-hued spin again, as if to belie any suggestion of mass illusion. The second spin had scarcely ended when the third began. This time the colours were richer and faster, pouring from a flying hub that had lost its outline in the whirling ball of kaleidoscopic fire. With increasing momentum the sun continued its giddy motion and the mood of the vast assemblage changed from wonder to startled terror. For suddenly, as if its speed had detached it from the firmament, the sun, now blood red, hurtled earthwards. Its vertiginous fall was contrary to the laws of gravitation, for it plunged from side to side like a coin sinking through water. But, oh! its descent was deadly swift none-the-less, and as it neared the earth an

anguished cry of repentant fear rose from the tightly
packed crowd.

" It is the end of the world! "

The cry was taken up by a thousand voices and
echoed from one end of the Cova to the other. Some
in their abject terror threw themselves flat in the mud
and beat their hands hysterically against the sodden
turf. " God have mercy on us! "

" Mother of God, have pity! "

" Forgive us our sins! "

The heat radiated from the falling body was almost
unbearable. It stung the face and hands with such
intensity that the majority of the people could no longer
look up but cowered in panic from the immense globe
that threatened them. Then, even when it seemed that
nothing could arrest that headlong fall, the sun, as if
pushed by the volume of terrified prayer, began to climb
back to its former position and as it ascended it reverted
to its natural colour. Fixed once more in the
firmament, it rode serenely in the blue sky from which
the clouds had completely disappeared.

The promised miracle was over.

Avelino d'Almeida was among the first to come to
his feet. He was bathed in perspiration from head to
foot and his collar, immaculate less than an hour ago,
was now a limp mass. Absently he smoothed it with
shaking fingers and pulled his tie straight. He had just
experienced the most terrifying moments of his life and
he felt empty, and sick with shock. He scarcely
listened to the excited voices about him, but he gradually
became aware that something important was occurring

in the hollow below. A storm of applause was coming from the people near the tree and instinctively he elbowed his way downwards.

Lucia and her cousins stood up. It was a signal for general acclamation. Senhor and Senhora Santos, Olimpia and Manuel Pedro Marto, led the advance of the pressing thousands. The air was thick with queries.

" What did the Lady say, Lucia? "

" Did she tell you who she was as she promised? "

" When will she come again? "

It was the last question which pierced Lucia's abstraction and forced her consciousness back to those around her. " She will not come again to the Cova."

" Did she say that? "

Senhora Santos bent eagerly over her daughter. " Did she tell you who she was? "

Those in the immediate vicinity strained their ears to hear the answer.

" She said ' I am Our Lady of the Rosary.' "

Immediately the name passed from lip to lip with repeated ejaculations and hurried signs of the cross.

" Anything else, Lucia? Tell us, child! "

The child considered for a moment. " She said the Rosary must be recited every day and that the war would end soon."

This piece of information in its turn was wafted away to the extreme ends of the crowd.

" How soon did she say? Did she mention a date? Think, child."

" No," replied Lucia simply, " She said it would

end soon." Then, remembering the agony of the Lady's voice: " She said that men must no longer offend Our Divine Lord. She was very sad when she said this."

With ardent eyes her mother gazed at her. " You must tell Dom Agostinho." She was half afraid that the mention of the pastor's name would cause alarm, but to her surprise Lucia merely nodded her head.

Protectively the parents guided their children through the enthusiastic throng. Everybody wanted to see the young seers, to touch them, to hear from their own lips the message of the Lady, yet although the clamour of their voices was all about her, Lucia was scarcely aware of their presence. In her heart she carried a heavy sorrow. Although the Lady had not said it, the child knew that their monthly meetings were at an end, and for the moment, at least, life had lost its purpose and its joy.

Near the road, she met Dom Agostinho. She stopped in surprise. The priest looked older than she had ever seen him, his cassock shabbier, and the hat which he carried in his hand was caked with dry mud. His eyes were tired, his face drawn and worried. A sudden pity rose in Lucia's heart and hesitantly she approached him.

" The Lady wants a chapel built here in her honour," she jerked out the words and smiled timorously. The priest inclined his head as graciously as if she were a lady of nobility, but his lips never lost their tightly drawn line.

Dom Agostinho was cautious to the end.

Yet the barriers he had erected against the inroads

of the beautiful Lady of the Cova were slowly
crumbling beneath the hammerblows of what he had
witnessed. The behaviour of the children impressed
him almost as much as the solar prodigy. The
convinced and radiant crowd were loud in their praise
of the young visionaries. Royalty could receive no
greater homage, yet the children carried themselves with
considerable humility. They were, in fact, a little
fearful of the crowd and pressed closely to their parents.
Once, when a hysterical woman had grabbed at Lucia
and cried " O, chosen of God! " the child had shrunk
back; no trace of pride showed in her face, but it
blanched with a deadly fear.

The disinclination of the children to enjoy their
fame was but another enigma that kept the priest
writing half the night. He wrote a full unbiassed report
of all that had happened since he first interviewed them,
filling page after page of foolscap with his untidy
handwriting, and it was nearly dawn when he finally
laid down his pen. Then he read the report through,
made minor corrections, folded the papers and stuffed
them into a large envelope on which he scrawled the
address of Dom Joao de Lima Vidal, Archbishop of
Mitilene.

The affair of the Lady was out of his hands.

Seventy miles to the south, in the city of Lisbon,
another man was writing into the small hours of that
morning. He wrote rapidly and with feeling, pouring
out his thoughts and impressions on many sheets of
paper which he scattered carelessly over his littered
desk. Rarely did he pause, as if fearing to lose the

thread of his inspiration and only when he had signed
Avelino d'Almeida on the last page did he drop the
pen and press his hand to his tired eyes. Stiffly he rose
from the chair and crossed to the window. The curtains
were undrawn and the lights of Lisbon gleamed in the
darkness. To-morrow he knew the news of the miracle
at Cova da Iria would resound like a thunderclap on
the capital. Already perhaps the first details of the
stupendous happening had trickled through, but when
the full torrent of eye-witness accounts was unleashed
by the returning pilgrims, the Grand Orient would be
faced with a formidable enemy. The journalist
shrugged; he was no longer interested in governmental
reaction. He walked to the desk and arranged the
pages in correct sequence. This was his column for
Monday's issue of " O Seculo "; a different survey from
the one he had originally planned. He sensed that there
would be serious repercussions for himself as soon as
the paper was on the street, but somehow his prestige
no longer mattered. He had written the truth of
October 13th. He felt he owed that much to the
Lady of the Rosary.

He switched out the light.

CHAPTER EIGHTEEN.

SISTER Maria Lucia of Dolours sat at the latticed window of her spotless cell and gazed absently out on the high Galician landscape. On her lap lay a thick sheaf of paper, each page covered with her own handwriting—flowing, decorative symbols that twenty-one years ago were strange, baffling enigmas. " I want you to learn to read," had been the heavenly command and so she had learned to read and write, to sew and mend, to pray and wait—and of all these achievements the last had been the hardest to accomplish. At times her span of life seemed endlessly protracted to her impatient soul, which marked the passage of every second that brought it nearer its final release.

The nun glanced down at the pages and sighed. They had been a labour of love. On to the smooth white sheets she had poured her precious memories, undimmed by the passage of time, of the wonderful days when the Lady came to the mountain parish of Dom Agostinho. Poor Dom Agostinho! What a problem she had been to him! Yet now she could understand and sympathize with his native caution and even see behind it the wise hand of God. The bewildered priest had fought a stern battle against the Lady, but, perhaps, that was because deep in his heart he knew his prejudice was but a barrier raised in prudence against his eagerness to accept the fact that his parish, of all those

that existed in the world, had been singled out by the
Mother of God. Later, after that fateful October day
when the sun danced in the heavens, his inherent
kindness and generosity had enveloped them, the
problem children of his flock, like a protecting cloak.
As best he could, he had shielded them from the
natural inquisitiveness of the people, and once he had
preached a thunderous sermon against those who denied
" these unaffected children any semblance of private
life." Yet it was not until 1921 that she was able fully
to know the kindly depths of this strange man.

"Lucia," he had said to her at the presbytery,
which still held for her an atmosphere of frightening
austerity, " do you remember how you told me once
that the Lady requested that you should learn to read? "

She told him that she remembered, but she did not
tell of the long hours of anguish she had often spent over
the merest scrap of printed paper, trying vainly to
unravel the sense from the mysterious printed symbols.

" Well, Lucia, we have decided, the Bishop, your
mother and I, that you are to have an opportunity of
fulfilling the Lady's wish. I know you will be glad of
that. We have decided to send you to a school for girls
conducted by the Sisters of Saint Dorothy at the Asilo
de Vilar in Porto. Here you will learn to read and
write, and many other things until you are properly
educated." The priest looked earnestly at her,
unwilling to cause her pain. " The Sisters are very
kind, Lucia, and they will treat you well, and if ever
there is anything you need you can write and let me
know."

She had gone gladly into that strange new world of austere cleanliness and culture, where at first her coarse dress and uncouth manner had shamed her before the curious eyes of the other pupils. Yet she had no desire to return to Estremadura, for all that bound her to her mountains was sundered. The Lady would come no more to the Cova, and Francisco and Jacinta no longer walked the earth.

" Soon," the Lady had said, " I will come to take Jacinta and Francisco to heaven." Yet She had allowed them to see the fulfilment of Her promise before summoning them to their reward. Peace, their eternal petition, had come to the earth. From the burning sands of Africa and the blood drenched mud of Flanders the young men of Portugal had returned, weary, embittered, disillusioned, and, following hard on their heels, borne on the breeze from the barren plains of death, came a pestilence that struck as indiscriminately and relentlessly as shot and shell.

The picture of Manuel Pedro Marto alone in the kitchen of his home, with his shirt sleeves turned up above his bulging forearms, was as clear in the nun's mind as if she had seen it but yesterday. He was keeping vigil over an assortment of pots that bubbled loudly on the fire. His face was haggard and the perspiration gleamed on his furrowed brow. Yet he managed to smile at her when she came in.

" You find me the only member of the family on my feet, Lucia. The rest "—he waved the spoon he held in his hand—" like everybody else in Portugal, are down

with the pest.   I'm sure the children would like to see
you."

She went to see Francisco first; a pale, wasted
Francisco, and though he smiled a greeting when she
entered the room, his eyes were bright with a feverish
lustre.   His hands, resting on the white coverlet, were
almost transparent, and the inevitable beads were
grasped between his fingers.   His breathing was so
laboured that she had asked:

" Are you in pain, Francisco? "

He nodded his head, but his eyes brightened with a
sudden joy.   " I bear it all for the love of Our Lord
and Our Lady."   The words were painfully gasped and
seemed to drain the little strength he had.   He closed
his eyes and she tiptoed from the room.

She found Jacinta in the same room as Olimpia
Marto.   The child looked even worse that her brother.
Her chest heaved in sharp, irregular movements as she
fought for breath.   Her first words were of Francisco.

" Have you seen him, Lucia? "

" He is a little better."   It had seemed the right
thing to say.   " And so will you be very soon.   It won't
be long before we are going to the Cova again."

Jacinta turned her head to the wall.   " Is he
suffering very much? "

" If he is, Jacinta, he bears it all for love of Our
Lord and Our Lady."

Across the room Senhora Marto was watching
them.   Her hair, usually knotted primly on the top of
her head, now fell in long tresses on each side of a white,

stricken face. In her eyes was a naked, intuitive fear.

*   *   *   *   *

The nun turned the pages of her memories. The sadness of that distant time haunted her still. Death had brooded over the Marto farm like an expectant vulture. The whole village seemed locked in a strange silence and in the hushed whispers of the neighbours was the expectancy of disaster.

She had seen Francisco the day before he died. There was a terrifying change in him. His dark, disordered hair was the only contrast to the uniform whiteness of the pillow and his thin, pinched countenance, but his pale lips moved in voiceless greeting, and his eyes brightened with welcome. He was glad to see her. He moved his head with an effort and she drew near him, for once at a loss for words. From the kitchen the murmured conversation of the neighbours reached them through the closed door.

" Dom Agostinho has been here," whispered Francisco. " To-morrow I make my First Communion." He closed his eyes in ecstasy. " Do you remember the cave in Cabeço, Lucia, and the Angel of Peace? "

She nodded her head. She felt she dare not speak lest she unleash a storm of passionate tears.

" It will be like that again, Lucia." He seemed to relapse into a reverie. For a moment she stood undecided. Then, thinking, he slept, she was about to steal from the room when he opened his eyes.

" There is something I almost forgot." His hand emerged weakly from beneath the blankets, grasping a soiled length of knotted cord. " Take this. I was afraid Mamma would see it. I can't wear it about my waist any longer."

She took it tenderly.

"I'm going to heaven soon," he continued, "but I will pray to Our Lord and Our Lady to bring you there also."

Poor Francisco, how prophetic he had been! He died the following evening. His pure soul, fortified with the Body and Blood of Christ, winged in eager flight along the trail of the setting sun to the arms of the Lady.

Sister Maria Lucia sighed. The span of years had failed to erase the memory of the blinding grief of those days. Some part of herself had surely died with her childhood friend. Even the recollection of the Lady's promise and the realisation that Francisco had gone straight to heaven, did not entirely mitigate the sense of irreparable loss that clouded her world for many days afterwards. She could not bear to visit Jacinta until the first storm of grief had subsided. But when eventually she forced herself to go to the stricken house she reproached herself bitterly for selfishly nursing her own sorrow. Jacinta was unimproved and desperately lonely.

They cried helplessly in each other's arms before Jacinta said: "I didn't see him, Lucia. And, oh, I wanted to." Her little frame, pathetically thin, shook with the force of her grief. "But I know he is in heaven, praying for us and the world." She gulped back her tears and lay on the pillow. "The world will need prayers in this coming war. So many people will

die in it. Priests will be killed. What a pity it is,
Lucia!" The thin hands moved restlessly over the
bedclothes. "If men ceased offending God, the war
would not come, and such great numbers would not go
to hell." Her eyes suddenly dilated with fear. "I'm
afraid for you, Lucia. Soon I know I will die, so I don't
dread the coming war, but you—— When you see the
light in the sky that the Lady mentioned, take refuge
in heaven!"

She lay breathless for a moment and her eyes were
suddenly full of pity. "But you can't take refuge like
that in heaven, can you, Lucia? Still, when I am there
I will pray very much for you and for Portugal that
she may be spared the horrors of war."

How strange had seemed Jacinta's talk of war, but
a few months after the end of the most terrible the
world had ever known. The nun lifted her gaze to the
landscape, now shadowed with the purple mist of
twilight. The intervening years had fulfilled the terrible
prophecy. Even through the quiet, sequestered walls of
this convent where she had taken her final vows, news
of the Spanish Civil War had infiltrated. Shocking
tales of unheard-of brutality had disrupted the
contemplative atmosphere of this consecrated house.
Yet the unknown light foretold by Our Lady had not
appeared. Perhaps She who laboured incessantly for
mankind had succeeded in restraining the just wrath of
God. This Spanish conflict, confined between the
frontiers of a single country, was petering out, and
although it had been terrible in its ferocity, it had not
reached the proportions of the fury that was racking

the world when the Lady first came to the Cova. Yet
it held an element of the danger the Lady had
mentioned. A spark from the inferno of active
atheism that was Russia had ignited Spain.

Sister Maria Lucia recalled the problem that that
one word of the Lady had created for her. At ten years
of age the word " Russia " had meant nothing to her
except that it was some distant land inseparably
connected with the Lady's grief. How that childish
conception had grown through the years, until the evil
of the beast of atheistic communism stood forth in all its
naked ugliness—the greatest enemy of God on earth—
so ruthless and powerful that it had warranted a
personal visit of the Blessed Virgin in October, 1917—
the very month in which the godless doctrine was
passing through its birth throes.

The nun lifted another page of the thick manuscript
and revealed the photograph that she had carefully
placed between the pages a few minutes before. It was
a picture of Jacinta; not the vivacious friend of her
chilhood, but a strangely beautiful Jacinta with her
eyes closed in eternal sleep. Even now in the deepening
gloom it seemed that the hooded eyes would open at
any moment and reveal the dark mirrors of a spotless
soul. It was difficult to believe that their owner was
dead, and yet one could accept without undue surprise
that this picture was of Jacinta's beloved face,
miraculously preserved after her body had lain for
fifteen years in the vault of the Barons of Alvaiazere, at
Ourem.

The picture, sent by the Bishop of Leiria on the

occasion of the translation of Jacinta's remains from Ourem to the cemetery at Fatima, was the nun's most precious possession. It reminded her of her last visit to her cousin in the hospital at Ourem.

" The Blessed Virgin has told me," Jacinta had said then, " that I will go to another hospital in Lisbon and that after much suffering I shall die there alone. But I'm not afraid, for she *promised* to come and take me to heaven."

Jacinta's prophecy had been fulfilled to the letter. She died at the capital on Friday, February 20th, 1920.

*   *   *   *   *

While the mind of Sister Maria Lucia of Dolours bridged the gap of years, darkness had descended on the landscape outside and deep shadows filled the narrow cell. Not a sound disturbed her retrospection, and gradually she grew chilled in the lowering temperature. One by one the stars came out, until the whole vault of heaven was filled with golden diadems. The beauty of the night wooed the nun's spirit back from the past. Stiffly she rose from her seat and opened the window. The serrated horizon showed dimly against the luminous sky. Presently she knew the moon would come up and tint the world with silver. But that would not be for several hours yet.

She turned from the window. Even as she did so the cell brightened suddenly. She could see her narrow bed plainly and the large crucifix hanging on the white distempered wall. In surprise she turned to the window. Had she mistaken the lateness of the hour? She leaned again from the window. The outline of the mountains was now clearly defined against a lightening sky. With a wildly beating heart the nun waited for the silver rim of the moon to peep above the hills. But no moon appeared. Instead, hurtling across the sky came a broad red beam of light. Gradually it grew in dimensions and intensity until the whole land stood out in crimson relief, beneath a sky that seemed aflame. The stars were still visible, but now they appeared like sparks thrown up by some gigantic inferno.

Sister Maria Lucia sank slowly to her knees and while yet the curious streamers flashed across the sky she burst into uncontrollable sobs.

The mercy of God was not yet. . . .

The Lady could no longer restrain the hand of Her Son.